Vet School

Part Two

Chris Shivelton Queen MRCVS

"Vet School is full of invaluable information and advice, making it an essential read for anyone interested in a veterinary career - thoroughly recommended."
Joe Inglis BVSc MRCVS

VET SCHOOL

CONTENTS

Contents

Chapter 3: Finances — 142

Contents

VET SCHOOL

AUTHOR

Christopher Shivelton Queen BSc BVSc MRCVS

Chris has been writing and offering advice and guidance on all aspects of vet careers and vet school applications since he was a vet student himself. He graduated in July 2007 from Bristol University, having also intercalated to achieve an additional degree in Biochemistry. Chris has been in small animal practice since graduation, initially in Oxford and then, most recently, working in the Berkshire,

Hampshire and Surrey area. Chris has been presenting to prospective future vets for many years and wrote the first edition of Vet School back in 2009, establishing his own publishing company in the process and going on to publish books by professionals in other fields. In 2012, he struck out on his own, setting up Shivelton Limited, and established Vet School Success. In addition to his advisory work on veterinary careers, Chris is a technology enthusiast and has developed iPhone apps and writes on technology in the veterinary sector, both through his blog (www.thenerdyvet.com) and for the veterinary press.

Chris currently lives in Dubai, UAE, and when he isn't treating the city's small animals or working on his next book or article, can be found out training for triathlons, indulging in various watersports or leaping from various planes and helicopters in the name of fun (with a parachute on, mind!).

Having successfully advised scores of students over the years, many of whom return to contribute themselves, Chris is proud of the fact that Vet School has helped so many students fulfil their ultimate dream of becoming a vet.

"I would like to thank each and every one of the fantastic contributors who have given their time and benefit of their experiences and knowledge to make this book the enjoyable yet useful tool that is. Special thanks go to Caroline for her, as ever, exquisite illustrations. This is the fifth book that I have personally had the pleasure of working with Caroline on and seeing her graphics for the first time remains one of my favorite parts of the whole process of creating a book. Lizzie Lockett also deserves a special thank you and, again, has been a long-term collaborator and contributor to my writing. Luke Gamble, the legend that is, has been hugely supportive of my writing and in spite of being a Global Superstar has also been ready to drop what he's doing to help me out. Kimberley Marsh, who has kindly allowed her personal statement to be reprinted, and the plethora of students, vets and professionals who have contributed to this book all deserve mention. I am proud to consider every one of these fine people as friends in addition to colleagues. Finally, I would like to thank my friends and family for their enduring love and support during the writing of Vet School. Thank you all."

VET SCHOOL

ILLUSTRATOR & CONTRIBUTORS

Caroline Parkinson (Illustrator)

Caroline is a freelance illustrator currently based in Leamington Spa. She graduated from Loughborough University in 2004 and has worked as an art assistant and props finder for the children's television shows "Mr Maker" and "Charlie and Lola." Other projects include the short film, "The Cloud Factory" for The Arts Council, character animation for the British Animation Awards, and several comics for various anthologies, including the British science fiction magazine 'Murky Depths' and 'Factor Fiction Press.'

More examples of Caroline's work can be found on her website www.carolineparkinson.co.uk.

Contributors

Without the immense generosity of the various kind souls who have contributed profiles, allowed us privileged insights into their own working lives and career paths, and provided reviews and content for this book, Vet School would be a significantly less useful resource and far less enjoyable and entertaining read.

Each and every contributor has the same passion for education as I do and they truly lead by example, acting as sources of inspiration to those of you who may be contemplating treading similar paths.

VET SCHOOL

PRAISE FOR VET SCHOOL

Here are just a couple of the reviews Vet School has received. Its always great to hear your thoughts so feel free to get in touch, even if its just to say hi.

"I think vet school was great. It was full of helpful advice and information that would otherwise take a lot of Googling to find out. The case studies from other vets and vet students were really helpful. I didn't get amazing GCSE results but the book made me realise all was not lost and gave me great advice with my personal statement and work experience and I genuinely believe I owe my offer to some of the advice from the vet school book. In short I think it's God's gift to vet applicants".

Sophie Gates (student)

"Vet School has helped me in every aspect of my application: it showed me what to look for in work experience placements, what to include in my personal statement, what to expect at interviews and loads more. It's a must have for any potential vet!"

Georgie Holiday (student & Vet News Editor)

VET SCHOOL

PREFACE

Like many of my friends and colleagues, I wanted to be a vet from an early age. It was the singular ambition of my education, partly because of the lure of a varied and interesting career, but also because of the unwavering support and encouragement from my parents and teachers who rallied behind my young dreams. I liked animals, loved the outdoors and that was that; I was all set from about the age of ten.

I don't remember ever being asked what sort of vet I wanted to be though. Twenty five years ago, 'being a vet' said it all. Treating sick animals, indoors or outdoors, large or small – it was simply assumed that 'being a vet' covered all the bases. James Herriot here we come.

Today, things are quite different. 'Being a vet' hardly skims the surface when describing a profession that is so progressive and evolving that it includes top research scientists to specialist surgeons who singularly work on specific parts of specific species. Being a member of the Royal College of Veterinary Surgeons opens so many doors it is difficult to know which ones to knock at.

There is no doubt, knowing what you want to do from an early stage, helps you get where you want to go. It's also incredibly important to be happy when you get there. The hard work, dedication and focus that this vocation demands is absolutely worth it if it delivers your dream and fulfills your ambition. But appreciating all the fantastic opportunities that becoming an MRCVS presents is the key to making the most of them.

From the challenges you will need to conquer to get into vet school, to deciding what sort of vet you might choose to become, this excellent book is a unique guide in helping you appreciate the road ahead and equipping you for the journey.

From UCAS application through to interview technique, this book provides an informative and honest text that is essential background reading in knowing exactly what you are taking on when you decide to qualify as a veterinary surgeon.

For my part, I've no regrets. If I had my time again, I'd do exactly the same thing and I can't imagine being part of a more rewarding and enjoyable profession. Yet it's fair to say, I can't think of a single friend with whom I qualified who is the same 'type of vet' that I am. We all have chosen different paths and work with different species or in different fields of expertise. None of us knew that would be the case when we arrived at vet school on our first day, but that is the way the profession is moving and anyone wishing to become a vet needs to be prepared for understanding that 'being a vet' can mean just about doing anything you want with an interest in the welfare of animals.

So in summary, if you are considering veterinary as a career option— and all the wonderful, exciting directions it can take you — then this book will tell you all you need to know about the opportunities that await — it is just up to you to go for it. Good luck and stick with it. Your adventure awaits!

Luke Gamble BVSc MRCVS

Founder & CEO

Worldwide Veterinary Service

www.wvs.org.uk

WORLDWIDE VETERINARY SERVICE

VET SCHOOL

1 : INTERVIEWS

Okay, so your applications have been submitted on time and you've been anxiously waiting to hear from the vet schools, a wait that feels like an eternity. Why do the vet schools even bother to interview applicants when a lot of other courses simply allocate places based on UCAS applications and test results? The main reason is that training a vet is a long and costly process, with the vet schools, and profession, very anxious to ensure that the considerable investment that is made in such training is directed to the best candidates and that their students are going to a) finish the course and qualify as a veterinarian, and b) represent a suitable fit for the unique culture of the vet school itself. Although every vet school achieves the same in terms of training new vets, they each have their own styles of teaching and unique culture which makes attending each one a distinct experience, in much the same way that different companies have their own 'culture.' The vet schools will be asking themselves whether you, as an individual, are likely to enjoy their school's vet school experience and ultimately benefit from the training. I am sure that you would agree that spending many thousands of pounds on someone without a face-to-face meeting seems like quite a risky move so it seems only right that the vet schools take as much care as possible in choosing their new intake.

5

If you are fortunate enough to receive an invitation to interview then the first thing to do is massively congratulate yourself as it is a huge achievement in itself. Admissions tutors receive applications, read them and then make a decision as to whether your application is of sufficient interest to take it further, moving you closer to the coveted prize of a place, or to say no, in which case you'll receive a rejection. As such, an interview invite is a sign that they are very interested in you and that they can see sufficient potential in you as a future vet to spend the time and effort getting to know you better. Loads of applicants fail to make it past the initial application stage so an interview invitation is definitely a cause for celebration.

What are the benefits of interviews?

The main benefits are the following:

1. Expand on your statement. I would argue that it is almost impossible to convey all of your awesomeness in a simple UCAS application and so a great way to learn more about you, including how you communicate and think, is to meet with you face to face and have a chat. Having said this, most vet school interviews are, on average, about twenty minutes long so even that can feel like insufficient time to really let your true worth shine through. All the more reason to be well prepared and feeling confident before you head in.

2. The vet schools can verify that you actually wrote your own statement. This might sound incredibly cynical but the fact is

that veterinary is an incredibly competitive course and some students may be tempted to significantly improve the chances of their statement catching the eye of the admissions tutor reviewing it by enlisting the help of someone with superior statement writing skills. This may well do the trick and yield an interview but if it is clear that the person sat in front of them (ie you) and the person coming through in the statement in front of them do not sound like one another, then they may well conclude that you either plagiarised what you have written, which is a very serious offence, or that you had more than a fair amount of assistance in preparing it, neither of which are going to impress the panel. By meeting with you face to face, without anyone else present to help you with what to say, they can be sure that they're meeting the real you, and not a carefully crafted version of you on paper.

3. Simply get to know you better. The interview panel will be able to assess many factors from the moment they first meet you to when the interview is over and you leave. Everything from how you present yourself, to body language, tone and what you actually say, will help the vet school assess whether you are the sort of vet student that they want studying at their university and whether you'll be a potential asset to the profession. You simply cannot make such an assessment of someone on paper alone.

4. Enable you to ask questions. Any interview is a two-way process, with you having the opportunity to ask questions and learn more about the school and the vet course, thus satisfying

yourself that should you be offered a place it is actually somewhere that you would really like to study. One important thing to remember, however, when considering what to ask at interview is to ensure that you do not ask anything for which the answer is easily found in any of the widely available media, such as their prospectus or website. This would suggest, fairly or otherwise, that you haven't taken the time to learn about the vet school and the interview panel's reaction may well be to question your preparation and commitment to study at their vet school. Remember, you don't want to give them any reason not to want to offer you a place.

When do interviews take place?

With applications submitted to UK vet schools by the UCAS deadline of 15th October, there is a period of time during which the universities review them and draw up interview shortlists. The interviews themselves tend to start in November and continue through to March or even April in some cases, although the majority of candidates are interviewed during January and February. One of the key take-home messages is therefore that no news is good news, as if you haven't had a rejection from the schools you applied to then there is a very good chance that your name is on an interview list and your invite will follow.

What form do the interviews take?

The majority of the vet schools use the traditional system of inviting you for a twenty minute interview with between two and three people (the panel), drawn from the veterinary teaching and clinical staff, veterinary professionals, and wider university faculty members. You will be directed to an area outside the interview room, where you may well find yourself waiting anxiously with several other nervous candidates. My advice would be to try and avoid getting drawn into conversation with others at this last minute stage, as it is very easy to get all flustered and spooked before your own interview, especially if you end up talking with the one person who seems to have done all the right work experience, has all the right grades, and still had time to write an opera, direct a play, perform at the Albert Hall, and generally excel in life way more than you seem to have done. Every interview waiting area seems to have *that person* and so I recommend just focusing on quietly preparing yourself, even if that simply involves sitting there breathing calmly and visualising a great interview. Taking along a few of your work-experience references and reading those whilst waiting can be a great way to focus your mind, trigger memories and generally give your ego and confidence a bit of a boost, assuming of course that they're good references!

Once you get called in, you'll usually be directed to sit in front of a table, behind which the interview panel will sit whilst they speak with you. It is remarkable just how swiftly those twenty minutes can go by and before you know it you'll be shaking

9

hands, thanking the panel for their time and sighing with relief as you exit the room. After that its simply a case of fingers crossed and wait for the university's decision.

There's always one. Or three.

A few of the vet schools do things a little differently when it comes to interviewing candidates, and it's certainly worth knowing more about their methods if you're planning on applying to any of them.

The first is Cambridge, who tend to start interviewing candidates much earlier than the other universities and so this may well be your first. When you apply to Cambridge you don't apply simply to the vet school. Instead, you will apply to a college that accepts vet students, either directly or through an open application, by which your application is directed to a college not of your specific choosing. As colleges are kind of like mini universities within a wider Cambridge University, with much of your learning being facilitated directly through the college itself via tutorials and other such activities, you will probably find that you have at least two interviews. One will be with a member of the college staff and tends to be more focused on testing your general intellect, attitudes, personality and ability to think through problems, with the purpose of assessing whether you're likely to fit in well, thrive and also contribute to college life. My own college interview was, as I recall it, quite a surreal experience with the conversation at one point straying onto the question of whether Woolly Mammoths should be brought back to life. The second interview is likely to then be with a subject-specific tutor, most probably a member of the vet school clinical and teaching team who is linked to the college. This will focus much more on your application to study veterinary and may involve a discussion of your work experience, your ability to apply knowledge from your studies to a range of problems or scenarios, and will generally probe your interest in, aptitude for and likely ability to do well on the vet course. My interview involved me being asked to select an anatomical specimen before going into the room and I was then asked various questions relating to that item. In my case, I selected a model of a dog's hip and so ended up discussing hip dysplasia and arthritis. As with the other vet schools, the actual interviews themselves were about twenty minutes long and the time passed very swiftly.

Liverpool have adopted a system of 'mini-interviews', which they call Multi Mini Interviews. This system sees candidates cycle round a series of interview tables, with about nine small, five minute interviews being conducted in total. Each station has a specific focus, such as knowledge of the profession, ethics, your motivations for wanting to study veterinary, and your ability to think critically by considering a scientific paper. The interviewers have a standard set of questions and scoring system, with the argument being that this represents a much fairer way of interviewing and assessing candidates than that offered by a traditional twenty minute interview. As a candidate you can expect to be marked on such factors as your communication skills, awareness of relevant ethical issues, and whether the interviewer considered you to be a suitable candidate for the profession. Some liken this style of interviewing to speed dating and complain that there is insufficient time at each station to really develop a good level of conversation and communicate all that you might want to. Others really rate this method and welcome the variety and perceived fairness that it offers.

Nottingham, the newest of the UK vet schools, has a more developed and staged interview system, with similarities to the corporate assessment days that you might be invited to if you were applying for a graduate entry position in, say, banking or the like. There are three stages to the day for those invited to a Nottingham interview:

1. **Interview.** The first is a standard panel-based interview, about twenty minutes in length, and provides an opportunity to speak one-on-one with the interviewers about your application, work experience, and, well, just about anything really.

2. **Practical Aptitude.** This assesses your ability to apply your knowledge of biology, science, and other subjects to various scenarios, and may involve handling animal material and considering clinical information. It is not a test of how much veterinary knowledge you already have, but more a way of seeing how you think and whether you are able to take information, process it and apply your own existing knowledge

such that you are able to make reasoned and educated assessments. There is usually a series of stations, including rest stations, which you move around in order and have a set period of time at each during which to answer the question posed.

3. **Team Working Assessment.** A core feature of Nottingham's teaching style involves group work with other vet students and so it is important for the school to select students who show a good level of ability and aptitude for working effectively in teams. This doesn't necessarily mean that they choose the same type of person, as a team in which every member was a dominant, leader type would be as ineffective as one in which every member was a genius but couldn't explain their ideas to their teammates or make decisions. As such, a good team involves individuals with a complimentary set of skills and character traits working as one for a common goal. The interviewers will therefore be looking at how you interact with others in such a teamwork situation. The key with this is not to try and be someone you're clearly not. So, for example, if you're normally quite a shy person but have lots of good ideas don't think you have to go into this exercise pretending to be an alpha character and bossing others around. The mismatch will shine through and be obvious. Better to relax, be yourself, try your hardest and adapt to the team you're put with.

NOTE: At the time of writing this book it appears that the RVC in London are also starting to introduce a bit more of a practical element to their interviews. For example, you may well be shown a couple of anatomical specimens, such as a dog skull next to a horse skull, and be asked to comment on them. Whilst they may not expect you to know the detailed anatomical features of and differences between the two, they will be looking at your thought process and for evidence that you can think logically and apply sound principles to your arguments. So, in the case of the skulls, you could point to the fact that the horse can only open it's jaw a little way, which is an adaptation as a grazing herbivore who is suited to nibbling at grass compared to the dog, who has a relatively wide angle of articulation, enabling the animal to seize onto prey. A look at their respective eye sockets would also highlight the differences in adaptation, with the horse having eyes on the side of the head, enabling it to effectively scan the horizon for any sign of potential threat from predators, whereas the dog has forward-facing eyes, which enable it to better judge distances and thus stalk and catch prey. The key point is not that you get the answers correct, but that you a) don't panic and freeze, and b) calmly walk the interview panel through your thought process, which they will be assessing as being one compatible with a potential vet student.

How do I interview well?

The main answer to this question, like most, is to practice. There are very few times when practice does not make perfect and interviews are no exception. Now of course you can't accurately predict what will happen on the day or what the interviewers will ask so there is little point trying to do so. What you can do, however, is prepare to be a confident, well informed, communicative candidate who oozes with motivation, passion and an obvious burning desire to study veterinary at the university you are fortunate enough to be invited to an interview at. The vet schools are not looking for students who already know everything there is to know about animals and veterinary science - if they filled places with such candidates then there would be little need for vets schools at all. What they are looking for are the kind of students we have already discussed and it is these aforementioned qualities that you should be aiming to project on the day.

Interviewing, or indeed presenting, well is a product of a number of complimentary factors that ultimately work together to give the desired impression to your audience. These are, in no particular order:

- preparation

- non-verbal

- verbal

Preparation

Do you simply turn up to an important exam and sit it without any form of preparation? If you do and you do well then congratulations as you are a very rare breed. If, however, you are like the vast majority of us mere mortals then I strongly suspect the answer is "of course not!" You revise and you practice past papers. This is to a) ensure that you understand and can recall the important information that may well be required in the exam, and b) to familiarise yourself with the format, length and pressure of the exam. This latter exercise is effectively desensitisation at work, as you gradually reduce your initial, automatic, and ultimately unhelpful and damaging, response to a stressful situation. If you did go into an exam without any prior knowledge of the format then chances are that you would spend most of your time getting flustered about how long you had to answer the questions, the fact that you didn't have access to textbooks, and the general stress of being in an unfamiliar situation. This would clearly detract from the important task of getting on and understanding the questions and writing sensible answers in the time allotted. This is no different to an interview and going into one without any level of prior preparation and 'desensitisation' will likely lead to you feeling anxious from the moment you enter, with the result likely to be a horribly stressful experience. But how exactly can you prepare well for an interview, and specifically a vet school interview. Well, read on and we shall learn.

The Early Bird Catches The Worm

There is little point in starting your preparation the evening before your interview. This is akin to cramming for an exam: pointless and just results in misery for all concerned. You know that you're going to apply to vet school. You also know that the interviews tend to start around November and run through until about March. I would personally start thinking and planning my approach to interviews in August, or at least September, before you have even sent off your application. Just the very act of thinking about an upcoming event gets all of your subconscious neurones firing away and before you know it you'll be able to draw up a winning 'how to be awesome at interviews' plan in time for the 'season.' The sooner you start thinking about the interviews then the more time you will have to find out the format, and practice using this knowledge, request references if you haven't already got them, start reading around relevant subjects and generally morphing into an interview King or Queen.

Which Vet Schools?

Edinburgh

There is no point spending precious time practicing for multiple, short interviews if you are not applying to Liverpool, so consider which of the vet schools you are applying to and tailor the specifics of your preparation to them. Much of your preparation, such as background reading, and getting used to being questioned in formal settings, will be the same regardless of which vet schools you apply to but there are some subtle differences that it is important to be aware of when preparing yourself. After all, time is a precious commodity to a prospective vet student.

Any Useful Contacts?

Do you know anyone who is either studying at or has previously applied and been interviewed at the vet schools that you're planning on applying to? If so then why not get in touch and ask if they would be willing to give you some helpful insight into that school's interview, including any questions that might have been asked. There is no guarantee that the same questions will be asked of you but it can be useful to get a sense of the type of questions that might crop up during your interview.

Be Informed

As a future veterinary professional it will be expected that you are taking an active interest in what is happening to affect the profession, and to have an awareness of issues and news of relevance. A classic example would be the whole issue surrounding TB and badgers, which you would be mad not to have some knowledge of before heading to a vet school interview. Talk to vets, vet students, farmers, animal owners and anyone else who you consider to be involved in caring for animals. What issues are they talking about and consider to be important? Chances are that the same issues will be the ones on the minds of the interview panel. Try and get hold of copies of publications such as Vet Times, which most vets will gladly put aside for you once they've read their copy, as these are the very best source of up to the minute industry news and comment. You certainly don't have to go as far as keeping press clippings but making a few notes on a few relevant issues might not be a bad idea. If anything, they may well serve as a useful refresher before the interview itself. Other very useful, and regularly updated, sources of current affairs information include Twitter, where stories seem to break before they've even had time to be written, blogs, of which the entire world seems to now have one, and social media in general. In fact, you'll probably be able to get a great overview of the main issues affecting the profession in a single evening's sitting, but the danger, as with most digital media, is overload. Remember that you're not aiming to become an 'expert' on everything of relevance to the veterinary profession, especially if doing so is at the expense of the rest of your preparation and life in general, but rather to have a good overall appreciation and understanding of the main issues, such that you can at least partake in a conversation.

Statement - Know It!

Its not at all uncommon for an interview to be guided by what's written in your statement. After all, this is the first place that the vet schools get to find out something about you and so it is perfectly natural that it should act as a launchpad for further questioning. It may seem like a stupidly obvious thing to say but it is so important that you know your statement like the back of your hand, as any discrepency between what you have written and what you then say in an interview will come across poorly. Read your statement through and internalise it until you are virtually dreaming about it at night.

Mock Interviews

Much as a mock exam allows you to get used to exam conditions, identify areas for improvement and generally get better at taking exams, mock interviews do the same for your interview success. Ensure that you manage to do at least one mock interview as I guarantee that you will realise the benefits. It is important with any mock that you recreate as best you can the actual scenario that you are practicing for, including the sense of formality that an interview has. It is only by repeatedly putting yourself in conditions which accurately mirror the real ones that you will start to develop the skills and familiarity with the format that will enable you to focus your mind on the aspects of the activity that are going to enable you to excel, rather than worrying about the minor details over which you have no control.

No Friends or Family

As we are aiming to recreate as closely as possible the setting of a real interview, there is little to no point asking your parents, friends or siblings to conduct a mock interview with you as you are obviously on familiar and friendly terms with them, meaning that you won't feel that sense of formality and seriousness that the real interview will have and so won't be able to desensitise yourself to the pressure and anxiety of such a setting. Rather, ask your school if they can help by arranging a mock interview with a member of staff who you might not be too familiar with, or perhaps a school governor. Schools will often have links with local business people, including veterinarians, and so may be able to ask such professionals if they would be willing to conduct a mock interview with you. The result is that a) you will likely find yourself doing your mock interview(s) somewhere far more formal, and realistic, than at home, and b) will take the exercise as seriously as you would the real interview, something that is less likely if your best mate or mum was the interviewer. The feedback you receive from an unfamiliar, professional interviewer is also likely to be far more honest and constructive than that which would come from friends, who are naturally going to want to make you feel good about yourself. It is, however, really vital that you get to identify those things that you did particularly well, and thus need less attention and development, and, more importantly, those things that require work and that you can improve on before your actual interviews commence. If possible, try and arrange for your mock to be conducted by more than one person as this will more accurately mirror the real scenario and also result in feedback from more than one person, which is always handy.

Dress Like You Mean It

Would you turn up to your vet school interview in a pair of jeans and T-shirt? No, of course not, so why not extend the principle of a mock to your dress as well by going along dressed for the occasion. The point of everything we do with mock interviews is to make sure you feel as comfortable and relaxed as you can come the big day, and to prepare your mind fully for the event. Anchoring is a term used to describe a process by which our mind forms a link between verbal cues, physical objects, and other such triggers, and our emotional state and subconscious mind. So by practicing your interview technique, including recreating such factors as what you wear, your mind will anchor the feeling of confidence, knowledge and ability that you will develop through practice to such factors as your dress. The result is that when you put on the same sort of clothes on interview day, your mind will automatically switch itself to the same state that it developed during your mocks, and you are far more likely to stride into your interview feeling the same sense of confidence and preparedness, with positive results.

As for dress code, I am sure you can probably guess for yourself but a general guide would be to encourage the following:

Males - a smart, well fitting suit with creaseless/ ironed shirt, or smart pair of trousers, such as Chinos, with a similarly smart shirt. The issue of whether to wear a tie is down to personal preference in my opinion and is not compulsory. Smart, clean shoes are essential to finish off the interview look.

Females - there is perhaps a little more choice and flexibility for you, from the option of a simple yet smart skirt - no mini skirts, as we don't want the interviewers having heart attacks - and blouse, to the classic trouser suit, which can be worn with either a blouse or appropriately smart top. Needless to say, anything too low-cut or that otherwise exposes too much flesh should be avoided. A basic rule is to say that if your gran would approve then you're probably on the right track. Smart shoes, as above, will finish the look.

Timing & Location

Once you have confirmed someone to conduct your mock interview, you'll need someplace to be interviewed. This will probably be an office or classroom at school or, if with a local professional, at their place of work. Confirm the date, time and location of the interview and ensure you arrive nice and early, as you would on the actual interview, with time to sit quietly outside the room before being called in. Try and stick to the interview being no more than twenty minutes, as is likely to be the case with actual vet school interviews, although it is not a major issue if it does run over as all it will do is provide extra feedback.

If your school, or the person who has agreed to interview you, is not familiar with the format of veterinary interviews or would find it helpful to have access to a list of suitable questions, you could send them a copy of this book, as it offers a very extensive set of questions for them to either use or to serve as inspiration for their own ones.

Film Yourself

I am sure that like most people the idea of seeing yourself on video is beyond awkward and you'd rather not even contemplate the idea. It is, however, an excellent way of rapidly improving your interview skills and I urge you to overcome your concerns and fire up the camera. By filming and then reviewing your mock interviews, you will be able to see every aspect of your performance, from how you entered to how quickly and clearly you speak, to whether or not you have any potentially irritating tics, such as toe tapping or drumming your fingers on the table, which you might never have been aware that you even did. I firmly believe that reviewing video of your mock interviews is one of the most powerful tools in helping you to ace your vet school interviews, so go on, become a star.

Non-Verbal

There are two aspects to communication: what you say and how you say it (verbal) and then everything else (non-verbal). Many psychologists say that about two-thirds of communication is non-verbal, which makes it incredibly important and should figure prominently in your interview preparation. Non-verbal communication includes everything from the clothes you wear, your gestures and body language, to the level of eye contact you maintain during your interview. Each member of the interview panel will be making judgements about you, and whether they want you at their vet school, from the moment you walk into the room, based on such subtle factors as how you walk in. They can't help this as it is perfectly natural and we all do it., with 'first impressions' often being difficult to alter. Have you ever had a new kid start at school and thought 'nerd' the minute they walk in simply based on the fact that they might wear glasses? I would be surprised if you didn't jump to such a conclusion. It may well turn out that the same 'nerd' is actually relatively non-academic but instead an excellent athlete - a very different person to the one we initially thought we had based on subconscious character judgement as a result of non-verbal cues. You can, therefore, use this fact to your advantage.

Clothing & Physical Appearance

We have already touched upon this subject in the section on preparation, with the main advice being to go for smart and conservative. Your university interview is not the time to make a bold statement, so leave the cutting edge fashion in the wardrobe and dress in something your grandparents would approve of. The main reason for this is that you are looking to project an air of professionalism as you enter the interview, and the panel will be imagining you as a qualified vet greeting clients. Offer them the best image you can.

Another area to think about when it comes to personal appearance is that of body art and piercings. As we have mentioned, first impressions count for a lot and it is unlikely that the interview panel will be as young, and thus hip, as you are. As such, it is unlikely that they will see the attraction and general awesomeness of the lip piercing you have or the intricate tribal design tattoo over your shoulder and upper arm. Again, they will be assessing whether they can see you greeting and interacting with clients as a professional and most would consider such accoutrements as not being in line with such an image of the veterinary professional. This might well sound all stuffy, boring and old fashioned, and I agree with you that it is, but you have to play the game by the rules as they currently stand and appeal to your audience.

Body Language

The aim of practicing with mock interviews is to arrive at the point where many of the points we talk about here become second nature such that you don't even have to think about them, leaving your mind free to focus on the questions being asked. Entire books get written on this one subject and so I am going to offer some thoughts on where you can make real differences:

Smile - this is probably one of the most important, yet overlooked, methods for improving the first impression you make. Most of us will likely enter our interviews looking like a cross between the new kid at school and a baby deer stuck in headlights: terrified! Your interviewers will, of course, make allowances for this but it will still give the impression that you lack some confidence. Better to greet them with a nice wide, confident smile which says "hey, I am really pleased to be here and to meet you." Try it in your mocks as at first it will probably feel really forced and fake, although with time will become much more natural and make a more positive impression. The caveat to this, however, is to not overdo it. Once in the interview relax and although continuing to smile, when appropriate, is important, maintaining a fixed grin like the Cheshire Cat will simply make you look insane - not a great look for a vet!

Hand Shaking - a topic that many a business book will spend trees deliberating and dissecting. Basically, my advice with handshaking is that if the interviewers go to shake hands then reciprocate, matching the pressure of the shake, if possible, but avoiding either a vice-like-breaking-bones effort or the worst type of handshake of all, the limp fish whereby the shake is so weak that they might well wonder if you're actually still alive. If they don't go to shake your hand then I wouldn't take it personally. It may well be that you are the eightieth person they have seen that day and they're just over shaking hands with everyone.

Posture - shuffling in like you're at a funeral, with eyes focused on the ground, will get things off to a bit of a dreary start. Even if you're not the most confident person in the world, the interview entrance is the time for a little theatrical application, so remember to walk in with your head held high, shoulders back, and eyes forward as if this is the only place in the world that you want to be right now. The interviewers will see a strong, confident young person enter their domain and, by extension, a competent future professional, as opposed to a meek, mild mouse who might faint if startled, and is unlikely to be able to cope with the stress of a vet consult.

Posture extends to taking your seat. You'll likely be invited to take a seat by one of the panel. If you're not then politely enquire as to where you should sit as opposed to piling in and just grabbing the first seat you see, which may well suggest that you're a bit rude, or just so tired from walking all the way from your home to the interview that standing for a second more is impossible. When sat down, be mindful of how you're sitting. The aim is to appear comfortable yet engaged. Slouching back as though you're chilling on your sofa at home is not a good look and will scream lack of respect. A neutral position, with both feet planted firmly on the ground and a slight lean forward will do fine. Girls, if you're wearing a skirt then crossing your legs is perfectly acceptable. Basically, however you'd sit in front of the headmaster at school is likely to be correct and appropriate.

At the end of the interview, remember that the panel can still see you as you exit. As such, resist the urge to punch the air in victory if you felt that things went well, or traipse out with your shoulders hunched if you felt that things couldn't have gone worse. Walk out as you walked in and you'll have rounded things off nicely.

Gesturing & Nervous Tics - judicious use of hand gestures can really help to emphasise points that you're making but, like most things in life, can be overdone. Watch some YouTube footage of great speakers giving speeches and take note of how they use their hands to reinforce the messages they deliver. Get it right and it can really add to the picture of you as a confident young professional, but get it wrong, and overdo it, and you may end up just looking as though you're having a seizure. Again, review video footage of your mock interviews to see if and how you're using your hands whilst speaking. Another area where video can really help to improve things is in identifying any potentially annoying little tics or stereotypies that you do when nervous. Examples include toe tapping, face touching, finger drumming, playing with your hair, playing with papers or pens in front of you - basically anything that you might end up doing, usually with no conscious awareness of the fact, that might detract from what you are saying and the positive impression that you're aiming to give. They are the physical equivalent of saying 'um' all the time, and the first step to reducing them is to know whether or not you do any of them, hence the mock interviews and video.

Eye Contact - Have you ever tried to have a conversation with someone who just won't look you in the eye? It's really hard and the impression you tend to be left with is that the other person is either excruciatingly shy, rude or shifty. Although being shy is not going to prevent you from making a great vet, not making a good impression in an interview may well prevent you even getting the chance to try. Try and maintain a good level of eye contact with all members of the interview panel during your time in front of them, with a good policy being to direct approximately 50-60% of your eye contact toward the person originating the question and then evenly divide your eye contact time between the others. Regular, relaxed changes of gaze direction also work well as most people start to feel uncomfortable if stared at for too long. One oft cited technique is to draw an imaginary line between the person's eyes and mouth, forming an upside down triangle, and then to follow this line with your eyes whilst speaking with them. This will help ensure that you spend sufficient time engaging in direct eye contact with them whilst avoiding freaking them out by staring. Occasionally breaking the gaze, either by looking to someone else or down at your notes (if you have any) is another way to break any possible eye-contact related tension. See what works for you in interviews and when you're generally chatting with friends, family and teachers.

Verbal

This relates to what you say and how you say it in the interview. What you say will obviously be determined by what's in your personal statement and what questions are asked and the background knowledge you have. To this end it is definitely essential to review your personal statement before going in to your interviews and to also do a little general reading beforehand. Ask questions of vets, farmers, nurses and others when on placements and get in the habit of making succinct notes summarizing key information so that you'll remember them for your interviews. You should be comfortable discussing things like which diseases we routinely vaccinate pets against, for example, and I personally find it easier to recall this sort of information if I have previously written it down. Also get used to keeping an eye on the national, local and specialist press so that you're aware of and informed on the main issues of veterinary interest. You don't need to rush out and take out a full subscription to Farmers' Weekly! Rather, just get used to glossing over the news regularly and ask friends and family to keep their eyes peeled for any potentially interesting stories which they can keep for you. Local libraries and the internet are often excellent sources of up to date newspapers and journals and the benefit of using resources such as libraries is that they are usually free, which is always a bonus! As I say, you don't need to become the leading authority on all the issues affecting animals and vets but rather be able to offer an opinion on such issues as the debate surrounding TB and badgers when asked in interview. Staring back blankly at the interviewer if asked something on such topics will not do your chances of securing an offer any good at all so arm yourself with some knowledge and let it become part of your normal, daily routine.

How you answer questions is the bit that you can definitely practice and improve on. You may be a walking encyclopedia but if you're unable to string a sentence together or have a habit of muttering or rushing your speech then this knowledge will not shine through. As stressful as interviews are your aim should be to make sure you listen carefully to the specific question being asked, and if it is not clear then ask the interviewer to either repeat or clarify the question – they won't think this rude, unless of course you ask rudely, but will rather see someone who is careful and thorough, both excellent veterinary attributes. The reason this is important is that it is very easy to end up hearing the question you want to hear rather than the one that is actually asked. You won't get any brownie points for answering a completely different question to the one asked – in fact, you're more likely to just receive confused, blank looks. If you need a moment to think about the question and your answer then do so – do not just open your mouth and let words fall out without any control. We've all been there and done that – with me it's usually been in a social situation involving a girl I like! Don't be tempted, either, to use vocabulary that you wouldn't normally use in an effort to try and sound more cultured, educated and high brow. Chances are you'll confuse the panel, get yourself tongue-tied and end up sounding more like Tim Nice-but-Dim than yourself. Remember, a lot of the time vets have to simplify complicated principles and explain them to owners in laymans' terms. Get used to explaining things simply yourself – the interview panel will appreciate this.

One key thing to focus on doing is to pace yourself. Recording yourself speaking or videoing a mock interview will inform you on whether you're like most people and tend to speed your speech up to a million miles an hour when stressed. Recognise this and make a conscious effort, initially anyway, to slow yourself down. It might, at first, feel like you're speaking too slowly but you'll be amazed at the difference it makes and how much clearer and more effective at communicating you will become.

Keep explanations and answers to questions reasonably brief. Think of the length of time it normally takes for you to get bored when listening to someone talk and keep this in the back of your mind. Some people may think that the longer they speak the lower are the chances of the panel asking you about something you don't know. This isn't a good technique to follow and you run the risk of boring the interviewers or, worse, forcing them to cut you off mid-sentence so they can change the course of the conversation – an embarrassing thing to have happen and it abruptly moves the interview out of your control, which can be a difficult place to be. Again, do mock interviews and video them so you can analyse your performance. Practice is the key!

Interview Day

The big day finally arrives and you'll no doubt be nervous – this is perfectly natural so expect to feel this way. If you have practiced, done some basic research and know your personal statement then you should hopefully feel a lot more relaxed than many of your fellow interviewees. This will instantly put you at a distinct advantage so let this knowledge further allay your fears. One thing I thoroughly recommend is to treat your interview like you would an important exam. This means that your brain is the most important tool being exercised and it is therefore vital to look after it so it functions smoothly on the day as possible. So, make sure you get a good night's sleep before your interview. If the interview is a long way from home, or particularly early in the day, then seriously consider staying over in the local area. There are normally lots of B&Bs and hotels with rooms available and at decent prices – it will be money well spent as you'll turn up to the interview refreshed and relaxed rather than stressed and tired. It also drastically reduces the chances of some bit of bad luck, such as getting stuck in motorway traffic or train delays, from adding to your stress levels. The next step is to eat well and stay hydrated. Fueling your brain on a diet of caffeine and chocolate, as so many of us do during revision for exams, is not ideal and will leave you tired, jittery and even more stressed. You'll probably also look as bad as you're likely to feel! Thirdly, do not cram – it rarely works in exams and is as equally unlikely to yield results in your interviews. If you haven't put in the legwork prior to the big day then you're unlikely to pull it out of the bag on the day itself. Sorry but it's true. Relax the night before and give your brain some downtime to process and make sense of all the preparation you have done for the interviews. It will then be on form for you on the big day. By all means take some basic notes and a copy of your statement with you to the interview so you can calmly flick through them prior to the interview – this will keep you from worrying about what is going to happen and will prevent you from focusing on what other candidates are doing and potentially getting freaked out at the last minute by the student who seems to have been everywhere and done it all.

Leave plenty of time for traveling to your interview so that you can easily cope with any unexpected delays or 'getting lost' in the campus or building in which your interview is being held. Check that you know exactly where, as in which room, your interview is going to be and at what time it is. Aim to arrive 10-15 minutes before the actual interview is due to start and sit calmly and quietly outside until called in. If you are able to find out who will be taking your interview early on in the day and can call upon any current vet students you know to give some background information on the members of the panel that they know then by all means do it but don't get bogged down by this and don't do it if it's just likely to stress you out and distract you from focusing on answering the questions that are actually asked. There are a plethora of 'advanced' interview techniques including skills such as mirroring which are beyond the scope of this book and there is a danger that you can become distracted from the important aspects of the interview by focusing time and effort on trying to 'engineer' and steer the interview too much. With practice you'll end up getting good at doing all of these things anyway so don't dwell on them at this point.

Interview Questions

There are several different types of question that you might be asked at interview and although it is impossible to predict exactly what will be asked, you can certainly ensure that you are generally prepared so you know not to panic if you are asked a particularly testing question on veterinary ethics, for example.

There are several broad categories into which you can divide most interview questions:

1. Questions that you <u>must</u> prepare an answer for.

These questions are so likely to come up that failing to consider them beforehand would be foolish. They are nice questions – assuming you are prepared for them – as they allow you to settle in to the interview. For example, being able to explain clearly and confidently why you want to study veterinary, and especially at that particular university, will enable you to tackle tougher questions with more confidence when they are asked later in the interview, as you will be in your stride.

2. Questions you will be expected to know quite a bit about from either your A-level (or equivalent) syllabus or from work experience.

This type of question is hard to prepare for specifically and you will need to rely on the academic ability and hard work you have done to date in your studies to help you. Similarly, you should have done a decent amount of varied work experience by the time you are called for interview so try and relax and remember that if you've done the basic preparation beforehand then you'll be fine. This type of question is often expanded to move into the next type of question.

3. Questions that take you out of your comfort zone.

You will inevitably get this type of question at interview and they tend to be the ones that students complain about afterwards! Being asked a tough question, or one without an immediately obvious answer, is actually a really good sign as it means that the panel want to stretch you and really see how your mind works. This means that they're seriously considering you for a place and want to make sure you have the aptitude and attitude for the course. The aim of these questions is for you to extrapolate your current knowledge, either from your academic work or work experience, and apply it appropriately to the question at hand. The important thing to remember when faced with a question to which no obvious answer exists is to avoid getting flustered and either blurting out the first thing you think of or just sitting there like a rabbit stuck in headlights. There is no such thing as an impossible interview question but it is vital that you take a moment to think it over before answering. It often helps to talk through your thought processes as this will enable the interview panel to see how your mind works and they may even subtly prompt and guide you to help keep you on track.

4. Questions that can trip you up.

There are certain questions that offer you the potential to really stick your foot in it if you just blurt out the first thing that pops into your head. We will see some examples of this sort of question later in the chapter.

5. Questions which open up a debate.

These questions have no correct answer and you need to be able to show an appreciation of both sides of an argument and discuss them rationally, before offering your own balanced opinion. Questions on ethics often fall into this broad category.

It is the latter type of questions which tend to really help differentiate you from the other candidates and make the interviewers remember you at the end of a long day speaking with multiple students, all of whom will be broadly similar. The course is a lengthy one and they will likely be teaching you for a large proportion of it. As such they will want to admit students who can think for themselves, approach topics rationally and engage in interesting and lively debates rather than just being fact-regurgitation machines. If you are able to be this type of student then you will make their lives far more interesting and increase your chances of being offered a place.

Example Questions

There are about a billion and one questions that you could be asked by the interviewers, and some vet schools seem to have their own unique style and preferences for their interviews. What follows are some examples of questions students have been asked in the past and which may come up in one form or another in your interview. They can easily form the basis for many similar questions of your own design.

Introductory & Motivational Questions:

1. *How was your journey here today?*

This is a friendly, low pressure, question intended to ease you into the interview and help you relax in what will feel a very formal setting. Take the opportunity to engage in a bit of light banter before the interview is directed in a more formal direction.

2. *Have you been to the university before?*

If you attended one of the open days then say so and take the opportunity to elaborate, for example, by telling them which part of the open day you found most interesting. It is also a great opportunity to tell them if you have been to the vet school or university before in a non-official capacity, for example, to visit a friend who is studying there. This will demonstrate your determination, resolve and resourcefulness in finding out as much as you can about all aspects of the course and specific school. Needless to say, however, if your only visit to the vet school involved a midnight ninja-style climb over the wall then probably best not to mention this!

3. *What do you think of our prospectus/ website?*

You will have read this. Please tell me you've read this! If not then this constitutes a major own goal and you will have to be very good not to let the interviewers see this is the case. If you have then offer an honest opinion and tell them about the parts you liked. What did it tell you that was unique about this particular vet school? This could lead on to other topics of conversation, such as work experience.

4. *How do you think you're doing with your exams?*

This is a great chance to really sell yourself, so if you're doing well then say so and highlight that you are working hard. If you're not doing so well then unless it's glaringly obvious in your personal statement, referee report or general application then it's probably better to just gloss over this and reassure them that you are doing well – you don't, after all, want to offer them any excuse not to offer you a place. If it's possible try and steer the conversation onto a subject that you are particularly interested in and that has some veterinary focus.

5. *Why do you want to be a vet?*

This is probably the most commonly asked question of any prospective vet, and even qualified veterinary surgeons are asked this countless times during their lives. It is also one of the most tricky to answer well and so I strongly recommend you spend a decent amount of time sitting and pondering this. You must ensure that you have an interesting, succinct and convincing answer to this question whilst trying to avoid sounding like everybody else – not an easy task! Try to avoid the usual clichéd responses, such as "I love animals." A simple fondness for animals and fascination for science do not necessarily make you a suitable candidate for training as a vet. There is often an initial motivation that makes candidates think of wanting to become a vet. This may have been an early experience with a family pet at the vets, or inspiration found in books about veterinary, such as the classic James Herriot series, or TV programmes such as 'Super Vets,' which manage to capture peoples' imagination. Its hardly surprising that such influences encourage students into considering veterinary as a good career option. It is, however, what you did after this initial trigger that really tells the vet schools whether you have thought seriously about your career choice. There is no way of knowing what you are getting yourself into without doing at least a basic amount of work-experience. As you will have seen from the chapter on work-experience, the key is to gain as broad a level of experience as possible. This way you will stand a greater chance of seeing first-hand all the facets of being a vet in this modern age. It is not all fun and it is important that you are aware and able to acknowledge and discuss the negatives of the career as well as enjoying the numerous positives that come with being a member of this special profession. I personally know of people who managed to secure a place at vet school with little to no real work-experience and who subsequently discovered that it really wasn't what they were expecting and that the profession was not really something that they were going to enjoy being part of. It's a real shame to get to the stage where you've committed yourself to starting university before making this realization and having to change direction. That's assuming, of course, that you're jammy enough to get offered a place without having demonstrated a decent amount of experience in the first place!

Veterinary is a tough course and the admissions team need to be absolutely certain that the people they offer places to are going to stick it out and complete their training. This not only means ensuring that you have the academic ability to cope with the course – hence questions about how you're doing in your exams and science-based questions – but also that you have the focus, motivation and determination to really get your teeth into the course. There are numerous times during the five or six years of vet school where most of us have thought, "screw this! I want to do ANYTHING else!" We all have these moments. The key difference, however, is to select students who are then able to cope with the pressures, knuckle down and remember why it is they want to graduate as a vet in the first place. Being

how would you comfort a student
like this?

43

informed in the first place is a huge part of ensuring this focus remains.

Veterinary is not all about working in clinical practice either. Research, industry and teaching are all vital aspects of the profession and vets are as important in these areas as they are in treating and dealing with patients and their owners. Experience of or, if this is not possible, informed appreciation of these other career options is something else that it is important to communicate to selectors. You may not have any intention at present of entering veterinary research but, as we all know, things can change and it is important to be open minded – you will, after all, be trained in all fields of veterinary – and demonstrating that you are aware and would consider these other options will impress and reassure the admissions tutors that you are a serious candidate and not someone who can do well in exams and just figured veterinary might be fun.

6. *Why do you want to study at this university?*

This question is a test of both your knowledge of the university, especially the aspects that make it unique and different to the other vet schools, and also one of your motivation. These days you need to whittle down your choices of vet school before sending the UCAS form off so chances are that you did a pretty decent amount of research into each of the schools before making your choices. What were the deciding factors that made some schools stand out over others? It could be that there were specific, unique features of one vet school that made you prefer it over another and these are the kind of factors that will help answer this question. It could be that you have a particular interest in equine medicine and your research and discussions with current vets told you that one vet school had an especially skilled and renowned equine department or specific clinician. Maybe you are particularly familiar with the university and the vet school, having perhaps visited friends, and so know that you will enjoy your time studying there yourself. Any reason, if explained with enthusiasm, is potentially a good one and this is a good thing to role-play during your mock interviews.

I have consulted admissions tutors and students alike to collate a number of questions that have been asked, in some form or another, in previous year's interviews. Although intended to be a helpful feature please don't blame me if you don't get asked any of these questions – there are about a million different questions that interviewers could choose to ask candidates and one thing I am not is psychic. In fact, feel free to get in touch via Twitter (@thenerdyvet), Facebook (Vet School Success) or the website (www.vetschoolsuccess.com) and let me know what they did actually ask you – we can then help future years together. Having said all this, perhaps the interviewers will read this book too and get some ideas!

The questions I have seen tend to fall under several broad headings depending on the main aim of the question. These, as I see it, are:

1. Work-experience

2. Scientific basics

3. Veterinary basics

4. Motivation

5. Ethics

6. Thought-provoking

7. Topical issues

8. Miscellaneous – sometimes there are questions that just seem really random!

Work-experience

These questions are usually prompted by what is written in your personal statement and tend to start off requiring a description of what you saw and did and then probing a little more to see what you actually learnt from your experience. Were you engaged and paying attention or merely going through the motions and an idle bystander? Be sure to know your statement through and through and re-read any placement journals and notes so your placements are fresh in your mind. Also make sure to read through any references you have from placements as they will, again, remind you of details and also buoy your confidence.

1. *Tell us something about your work-experience.*

This isn't an invite to just list your placements – they will have your statement in front of them. What they want from you is to hear what lessons you learnt and whether there were any interesting experiences.

2. *Name an interesting operation you have seen.*

This will likely be in response to some mention of seeing some "interesting surgery" in your statement and/or if you happen to have a surgeon on the panel. If you specifically mentioned watching a particular type of operation (eg. a TPLO procedure, which is one technique used to manage cranial cruciate ligament injuries in large dogs) then be fully prepared to expand your answer and discuss it with the panel. This does not mean you should go away and memorise chapters from surgery textbooks. Asking the vet who performed the surgery to explain the main principles and being able to understand and relay this information will be sufficient. After all, you are applying to be trained as a vet, not demonstrate that you already know everything.

3. *What are the main lessons you have learned from your work-experience?*

This is a potential follow-up question to the first and it is important to highlight the breadth of experience you have. Try to make it clear that you have learnt that veterinary isn't just all clinical and that there are numerous hats that modern day vets must wear, including that of business-person. It is also a people-centred profession so demonstrate your awareness of that fact in your answer. Where possible try to illustrate your answers with specific examples. For example, "When I saw practice with a small animal vet doing a heart scan, I…."

4. *What did you see and learn when you went lambing?*

Again, a question prompted by a specific placement mentioned in the personal statement and it is important to listen carefully to the question asked and ensure you answer both parts – descriptive and reflective. You may have helped actually deliver some lambs, and so will be able to explain why intervention was required, or perhaps you had to help the farmer manage an outbreak of watery mouth (an E.coli infection which causes diarrhea and loss of lambs), and so can discuss the treatment and measures taken to prevent any further outbreaks. You should make sure to pay attention and quiz the farmer on fundamental flock management during your time on the farm. This includes things like when the ewes are mated, how the farmer knows when they have been, how the ewes are fed prior to, during and then post-lambing. It is easy to get drawn into the excitement of lots of baby animals running around and forget to take in the bigger picture of what is involved in running a farm. What are the challenges that the farmer faces? What issues are affecting them and their farm? How are they overcoming them? Farmers are generally pretty outgoing, sociable people and will enjoy telling you about their farming experiences and opinions. Make the most of having them there in front of you!

Ask Richard

5. *When you went to the abattoir, what did you see? Did you enjoy the experience?*

If you are lucky enough to be able to secure some work-experience at an abattoir then you may be asked this question. Managing animals through the food chain is an important part of being a vet, especially during your training phase and for those vets engaged in large animal work. Even if you are fiercely vegetarian or opposed to meat you will be expected to undergo and complete training in aspects of production animal management so this is a vital area to be aware of. If you do spend time at an abattoir pay attention to what happens at each stage of the process – from lairage to inspection and final finishing of the carcass, the process has been carefully designed to be as hygienic, efficient and stress-free to the animals as possible. A lot of the science of meat, and indeed other food, production is covered extensively as part of veterinary public health courses during your vet training. The question of whether you enjoyed the experience is an interesting one. I can't imagine anyone really 'enjoying' spending time at an abattoir, especially if you have never experienced anything like it before, but the interviewers want to see that you respected and learnt from the experience.

6. *Talk about your week at the dairy farm.*

As with other work-experience questions the key to answering this well is to describe what you saw and experienced during your time, highlighting any particularly interesting experiences. Try and keep your answer reasonably succinct as it would be easy to start waffling with such an open-ended and broad invite to talk. Again, this will probably lead onto more focused questions, such as "you mentioned you dealt with a difficult case of calving. Can you tell me some more about that," as one student was asked. If there is something specific that you mentioned in your statement or that you want to discuss in more detail then be sure to mention this in your initial answer. For example, if you helped disbud calves then perhaps say something along the lines of, "I found the experience of helping with disbudding particularly interesting." This should, hopefully, prompt the interviewer to invite you to speak in more detail about this experience.

7. *What are the realities of being a vet?*

OR

8. *What are the key attributes a vet should have? Do you have these?*

This question should be fairly easy to answer after reading this book and certainly after doing a good amount of work-experience. The interview panel will want to see that you have thought carefully about the pros and cons of a career in veterinary and that you realize it isn't all fun and can, at times, be very stressful. A good way of answering this would be to start by saying something like, "Vets need a range of skills and specific attributes to be effective at their jobs and these include…." Finish your answer on a positive note by highlighting a positive aspect of the profession – perhaps the one feature that attracted you in the first place, or a positive attribute that you know you possess and can offer evidence in support of. You really want the interview panel, in their minds, to see you as a vet or at least studying to become one at their vet school, so when giving your answer, or listing attributes, make sure to refer to your own experiences so they start to associate the 'vetty' attributes with you.

good
work lots
of different
people
- I discovered
how much
I like
working with
people during
my time at waitrose
I don't really have any enemies!

51

Veterinary Basics

These questions test your observation and motivation during work-experience placements as they are all on topics that will have been encountered during time spent on farms, in clinics and working in other animal settings. Some you will be expected to know, such as which diseases we vaccinate puppies against, whilst others may fall into the 'thought provoking' category whereby you would not be expected to know the answer but should be able, through what you've seen and already know from school, to make educated attempts at answering. The latter type of question, whilst being terrifying at the time, actually signals a positive note about how the interview is going. This is because they will only try and stretch you when they are seriously interested in you as a potential vet student and so want to see, in more depth, how your mind works. Contrary to some belief veterinary interviewers do not enjoy grilling students and making them sweat – its just as uncomfortable for them as it is for you – and if you are really struggling and the interview is not going so well then they will be more likely to ease up on you and ask some lighter questions, thus easing you through to the end of the interview. Having now said this, if you do feel like you're flying through the interview and every question is easy don't assume that something is wrong and you're in trouble – maybe they are just nice people and/ or you're just a superbly knowledgeable and well-practiced candidate!

1. What do you vaccinate dogs/ cats/ rabbits against?

Vaccinating animals is a fundamental part of clinical veterinary medicine, not only in small animal practice but equine and farm practice as well. If you have spent time observing small animal practice then I daresay you will have stood in on quite a few vaccination consultations. How many of you really paid attention to what was being given and why? I remember standing in on hundreds, if not thousands, of vaccinations and still having trouble recalling what diseases we were protecting pets against. It is easy to find yourself drifting off, especially when it's the thousandth jab you've watched the vet give and it's a warm day, but it is important to make sure you know something about vaccination. It would, after all, look a bit poor if you were asked this question and your only response was a blank stare – the panel would, quite rightly, wonder what you'd actually done during your time in practice.

Dogs

We routinely vaccinate dogs in the UK against the following diseases:

- Distemper

- Hepatitis

- Parvovirus

- Parainfluenza

- Leptospirosis

Puppies are vaccinated at 8 weeks of age and then receive a second injection at 10 weeks. The advice to owners is to then wait a further week before their puppy should be safe to start going for walks in public areas, such as parks, where un-vaccinated dogs may have been. Dogs get all of the above boosted a year later and then we only boost all of the components every three years, with Parainfluenza and Leptospirosis being the only diseases which dogs are vaccinated against every year. The reason is that immunity to diseases such as Parvovirus is much more lengthy than these other two and so it is considered unnecessary to vaccinate against them every year. This is in response to greater levels of research into the area of vaccination and accusations from various groups that vets over-vaccinate animals unnecessarily. If an annual booster is missed and the dog lapses then a restart course is normally required, comprising a repeat of the puppy vaccination process.

Although the diseases above form part of the 'core' vaccination for dogs, it is also possible to vaccinate against kennel cough. Despite its name, kennel cough, or infectious bronchotracheitis (inflammation of the windpipe) to use its full name, is not exclusive to kenneled dogs and is best thought of in the same way as the common cold in as much as it is a syndrome caused by a number of different pathogens, both viral and bacterial, which contribute to the development of disease. As such, the vaccine, which is live and given as a small volume of liquid up the nose, is not 100% protective and dogs can still develop kennel cough. This is important to make owners aware of as it is highly embarrassing for all parties involved to have an irate owner march their dog in and angrily enquire as to why their dog is coughing like it has a fifty-a-day habit in spite of being vaccinated. The kennel cough vaccine affords immunity against the main causes, with clinical disease normally being limited to a dry, hacking cough of approximately two weeks. The main risks are that the condition is highly contagious and so can be easily spread through shared air spaces by coughing dogs, and can progress into more severe respiratory disease such as pneumonia, especially in very young, old or debilitated dogs. It is the fact that it spreads so easily via shared airspaces that means most kennels will ask for dogs to be vaccinated against kennel cough before being admitted.

Dogs travelling under the PET scheme are also required to be vaccinated against rabies, which is currently not present in the UK but endemic in many countries across the globe, including Europe. As long as the animal is old enough to be vaccinated, has a readable microchip implanted (and is thus identifiable) and has been given the rabies innoculation, then a passport can be issued. It is important to keep the rabies vaccinations fully up to date and to check that the pet's microchip can still be read, so as to avoid any travel issues.

Cats

Cats are vaccinated against the following diseases:

- Feline Calicivirus (FCV)   *a must*

- Feline Rhinotracheitis ('Cat Flu')   *a must*
  /Herpesvirus type1
- Feline Infectious Enteritis (aka Panleukopaenia)   *a must*

- FeLV (Feline Leukaemia Virus)   *a must for outdoor cats*

Some people also vaccinate their cats against Chlamydophila.

Kittens are vaccinated at 9 weeks of age and boosted three weeks later at 12 weeks. They then receive annual booster vaccinations thereafter. The first three diseases shown above tend to be referred to as 'core' vaccinations with FeLV only really applicable to cats who are going to be going outside and potentially contacting infected cats. Some advise to give the FeLV injection under the skin on a back leg, with the right often being used. This is due to the fact that there have been cases of cats developing sarcomas (a type of tumour) in response to being injected with FeLV vaccine. Although the risks are minimal, and certainly do not preclude vaccinating against the disease, it is proposed by some that it is best to inject in a leg as it is easier to manage a sarcoma by amputating a leg than it is to remove an aggressive tumour from the scruff. This seems to be less of an issue as vaccine technology moves on and I personally no longer adhere to this line of thinking, opting to inject in the scruff as the vast majority of the profession do.

Like with all vaccines, it is important to carefully follow the manufacturer's guidelines and to perform a thorough clinical exam of each animal before administering one to them. This includes starting the primary (puppy or kitten) course at the correct time, as giving them too early can result in residual maternal antibodies affecting the efficacy of the vaccine, which may not work as well.

Rabbits

The two diseases that we routinely vaccinate rabbits against are:

- Myxomatosis

- Rabbit Haemorrhagic Disease (RHD)

Myxomatosis is spread by fleas and wild rabbits act as a reservoir for the infection, which causes swelling of lymphoid tissue, especially the eyes, nose and genitals, and ultimately leads to death. There are now combined myxomatosis and RHD vaccines, which are given once per year, offering full annual cover. RHD is spread easily by flies and can affect all rabbits, including house bunnies.

2. *Why would you castrate an animal? How would you spay a cat?*

The key to this first question, like most, is not to jump in with the obvious answer – which is to prevent unwanted breeding – but to take a moment and think about the question before answering. Doing so will ensure that you remember that there are a number of reasons why we castrate and spey (neuter) animals: prevent unwanted breeding; reduce the risk of certain types of cancer later in life – for example, speying bitches before they are a year old reduces their lifetime risk of mammary (breast) tumours to less than 5% compared to 25% for entire bitches. We also neuter animals to dramatically reduce the risk of specific conditions such as pyometra in females. This condition basically translates as 'pus' (pyo) and 'uterus' (metra) and is what is says on the tin: an infection of the uterus, of which there are basically two forms – open and closed. The former is when the cervix is open and the infection can drain, meaning that we can observe a discharge, and is less serious than the latter, which means that the infection is allowed to rage behind closed doors (a closed cervix). Usually the first signs of a closed pyometra are a bitch presented with a history of recently finishing her season, although it can occur at any time, who is drinking more than normal, dull, depressed, innappetant, and 'just not right.' Investigation may reveal a fever, raised white blood cells on a blood test and a fluid filled uterus on xray or ultrasound. Closed pyometras are best treated surgically by removing the infected

58

uterus, with the ovaries removed at the same time, as you would normally when speying (an ovariohysterectomy). Another option is to manage medically initially, with the aim being to reduce the infection and risk such that surgery to neuter can then take place when the risks are less. This condition is an important reason to advise speying of females, including the fact that treating a pyometra surgically costs considerably more than a routine, elective spey, so there are economical indications for it as well as medical. Some owners aren't sure whether they want to breed from their bitch and so I normally discuss the subject with them at each of their check-ups and advise them of the signs to look for with regard to pyometra.

Behaviour is another reason to neuter animals, with early neutering of males certainly resulting in a reduction in the display of characteristic male traits, including aggression. Castrated males are less likely to be disobedient on walks and run off if they smell a bitch in heat – they can smell one miles away! One note of caution here though: some behaviours may become ingrained and become part of the dog's character, especially if castrating later in life, and so removing their testicles may not always reverse or temper the undesirable behaviour in which case behavioural therapy may be required.

The question of how you would spey a cat is a test of your observation whilst in practice. You would, unless very unlucky, have watched at least one cat spey and so should be able to answer this. In the UK we routinely remove both the uterus and the two ovaries (an ovariohysterectomy) via an incision (surgical cut) in the left flank, just in front of the left hind leg. Outside of the UK, and in cases where either the owner requests it or the uterus is particularly large, such as in pregnancy, speying may be done via a midline ventral (along the underside of the abdomen) incision, like in bitches. The abdomen is entered, ensuring that you penetrate the peritoneum, which is a little like a layer of cling-film that covers the inside of the abdomen, and the uterus identified. I then follow each uterine horn forwards until I reach the accompanying ovary. The ovarian pedicle, which contains the blood vessels supplying the ovary is then clamped with two to three clamps, and a ligature placed to close off the blood supply. Each surgeon will have their own preferences for the number of ligatures placed, the material used and the method of placing them. I, for example, routinely place one catgut (absorbable material) ligature which I transfix, which means I anchor it within the tissue of the pedicle making it less likely to slip. Once the ligatures are placed, the clamps are separated to break the pedicle. The end of the pedicle is checked for any signs of bleeding before being released back into the abdomen – it is important to check them carefully and be confident in the security of your ligature as when you release they tend to pop back into the depths of the abdomen very quickly and if you subsequently find it does bleed then they can be tricky, not to mention stressful, to find again. Once you have repeated this for the other ovary, the broad ligament is carefully blunt dissected, which means broken down with your fingers, to free up the uterus and allow you to clamp and ligature the cervix, in much the same fashion as for the ovarian pedicles. Once all of these

clamped then ligated

stages are complete and the uterus and ovaries are removed in one piece – it is important to check that you have all of the ovarian tissue as leaving any 'ovarian remnants' will result in continued oestrogen production and all the characteristics of an unneutered female – the abdomen is closed, including the peritoneum, using a strong, absorbable suture material. I then bring the subcutaneous tissues, like the fat that just sits under the skin, together with some sutures before closing the skin either with intra-dermal sutures, which dissolve and therefore close the skin without any stitches showing, making for a very neat finish, or non-absorbable skin sutures (usually nylon) which are then removed in about ten days. The surgery itself is only one part of the procedure and it is important to be aware of and understand what we do both before and after the operation and why. Pain relief is provided before the surgery, and sometimes continued for a few days after the operation, and a lot of vets will advise the use of a buster collar to prevent the cat licking at or chewing their stitches, thus reducing the risks of infection and opening up the incision. It is important to advise the owner to keep their cat in after the operation and, ideally, until any stitches are removed. Some vets give antibiotic before surgery whereas I personally do not, unless there is any concern that the uterus is previously infected, as the risk of infection should be very low if correct surgical technique and asepsis is used. This is down to personal veterinary choice, however, so talk about what you have seen and be sure to understand why things are done the way they are.

3. *How do you stop a cow being in pain from labour?*

You will most likely be asked a question like this if you have written something in your statement alluding to the fact that you've witnessed or helped with a calving. There are two considerations when thinking about pain associated with calving: one is to provide pain relief during the actual process; with the second to think about pain relief afterwards, which lasts a decent period of time. It is also important to consider the implications of your answer. For example, administering an epidural (injection of local anaesthetic into the fluid supporting and surrounding the spinal cord), and thus suppressing the nervous impulses entering and leaving the spine at the point of action, may be appropriate analgesia (pain relief) if you are performing a caesarian section or pulling the calf out manually yourself, but would be wholly unsuitable if you were then expecting the cow to push on her own, as the anaesthetic prevents such muscle activity. Pain-relief which doesn't interfere with natural labour, and which is usually given at the time of caesarians as well to provide longer-lasting analgesia, is provided in the form of a NSAID (non-steroidal anti-inflammatory) injection, with meloxicam a favourite choice as it lasts up to 72 hours.   (metacam)

4. *What causes mastitis?*

Like the neutering question, this requires a moment of careful thought before just jumping in with the obvious answer, that being 'bacteria,' which although correct is not the entire story. Mastitis is inflammation of the mammary tissues and is something we occasionally see in all animals, including pets, but are most familiar with when talking about dairy cattle. It is a particular problem in dairy practice as the milk from cows with mastitis cannot be added to the tank and so represents lost revenue to the farmer. Cows with mastitis also cost the farm money through the need for antibiotic treatment and the fact that they still need feeding etcetera even though their milk is not being sold. It also represents a welfare issue for farms, with nine out of every ten cases currently seen being due to cow-adapted strains of the environmental bacteria Streptococcus uberis. This bacterium enters the mammary gland via the teat canal and 'hides' in white blood cells. The main problem is that when the cow is treated with antibiotics, the bacteria remain within the white cells with the antibiotic being cleared faster than the infected white cells meaning that recurrent cases are common. As such, a lot of vets extend the treatment period in cases where Strep.uberis is confirmed, the aim being to ensure that the bacteria emerge into an antibiotic rich environment and are thus killed. The bacteria that cause mastitis can be broadly divided into two categories: environmental pathogens, such as Streptococcus uberis and E.coli, which are present in the environment; and contagious causes, including Staphylococcus aureus, where it is generally better to dry the cow off than risk having it potentially spread the bacteria to other cows in the milking parlour.

Scientific Basics

There may well be considerable overlap between this type of question and the one probing basic veterinary knowledge, as the latter often relies on the former to be able to expand and explain your answer. Veterinary is, at the end of the day, a science and it is no accident that candidates are expected to be accomplished in the sciences. Are you able to apply and expand on the scientific training you have already received or are your high grades in the subject simply a result of your photographic memory? These questions should be able to differentiate those who can use their science, as you will be expected to do every day of your life as a vet student and vet, from those who simply suck up information and spew it out with no further thought. It's a great idea when answering these questions to add veterinary relevance, even if the original question does not immediately have a veterinary angle. Doing so will remind the interviewers that you are here to secure a place on their vet course and they will be better placed to start imagining you as a student of the school. Cambridge, apparently, place more emphasis on assessing each student's level of genuine interest in the science that underlies health and disease in animals. As such, it might be that questions about stem cells, the nervous system or bovine TB could quickly move onto disarmingly simple follow-ups, like "so, what is a cell exactly?" or "can you draw a neuron on this piece of paper," or even "what do you think are the main differences between a bacterium and a virus?" Colleges sometimes send candidates a questionnaire including a slot for suggesting two or three topics for discussion at interview. This, like the personal statement, can be very helpful and can then form a framework for questions. Both are, however, potential traps if you put down something 'clever' which you may then regret including if you are unable to remember anything about them!

1. *How does a vaccine work?*

Vaccinations form a healthy part of the daily workload of a vet in practice, especially small animal vets, and understanding your 'product' is essential to be able to convincingly and reliably advise your clients on their use. Vaccines work by stimulating the body's immune system in one of two ways and leads to a persistent, retained level of responsiveness which enables the animal to effectively mount resistance and fight infection if exposed at a later stage. There are two main types of cell actively involved in immunity: B-cells, which produce antibodies; and T-cells, of which there are a few types, but which are involved in directly targeting diseased and antibody 'labelled' cells. Vaccines can be one of two types: live, or attenuated, in which the pathogen (bacteria or virus) is treated to weaken its ability to produce disease whilst still being able to trigger an immune response; and killed, or inactivated, in which the pathogen is no longer able to cause disease but will still lead to antibody production. The latter type of vaccine can either include the entire killed pathogen or carefully selected components which are known to be important in stimulating antibody production, such as surface membrane proteins. Killed vaccines tend to produce a weaker and less persistent level of immunity compared to live vaccines and so it may be necessary to give more frequent boosters if using a dead vaccine.

2. *What is a hormone?*

Hormones are important chemicals within the body which act as signals, and are produced and released from one type of cell whilst interacting and causing a specific change in another type of cell. A huge number of processes within the body are controlled by the action of hormones, from reproduction to glucose metabolism and even the feeling of being full and satisfied after eating. Knowledge of hormones and how they work is important in medicine, and veterinary is no exception. As vets we actively manipulate hormonal systems, for example by neutering animals, and are able to recognise, diagnose and treat a range of hormonal disorders, ranging from diabetes to Cushing's Disease.

3. *How do hormones work? How are they carried around the body?*

Hormones are produced by specific cells, such as the beta cells in the pancreas, which produce insulin, and either diffuse to act on adjacent cells (paracrine signalling) or are transported via the bloodstream to different parts of the body (endocrine signalling). Cells respond to a specific hormone if they have a receptor for it expressed on their cell membrane – a little like having a specific keyhole which can only be opened when the correct key is used. The interaction of the hormone with the receptor leads to a series of changes within the target cell and an appropriate response, such as an increase in the rate at which heart muscle contracts in response to adrenaline. There are a number of good veterinary examples of hormone systems and conditions that we see in practice and which can be used as relevant examples in your answer, thus impressing the panel with your level of applied scientific knowledge. These include:

- **Hyperthyroidism** – an overproduction of thyroid hormone and an important differential in cats presenting with weight loss, especially if over the age of eight. Other signs include a rapid heart rate, weight loss in spite of a good appetite (paradoxical weight loss), increased vocalisation and a change in behaviour, including increased aggression.

- **Hypothyroidism** – an underproduction of thyroid hormone and more often seen in older dogs than any other patient. Affected animals can show a range of signs including focal hair loss, weight gain and a slow heart rate.

- **Diabetes mellitus** – a failure to produce *type 1* or to respond *type 2* to insulin. As a result glucose is not taken up by cells and signs can include increased thirst and urination (polydipsia and polyuria), weight loss, cataracts and vomiting.

- **Cushing's Disease** – an overproduction of cortisol, the 'stress hormone.' This can have a wide range of effects and so there are many potential clinical signs including increased drinking and urination, the development of a pot-bellied appearance, thinning of the skin and poor wound healing.

4. Why do animals need a hormonal and a nervous system?

The hormonal and nervous systems are effectively biological communication systems which maintain homeostasis – in other words, keep the animal in a stable, healthy state. There are benefits to having both systems in operation as they complement each other. The nervous system includes both the central nervous system and reflexes, which are essential in helping animals react rapidly to potentially harmful stimuli, such as being burnt. Hormonal systems tend to regulate metabolic processes, such as sugar control, and also influence behaviour, for example, the influence of the reproductive hormones. Both systems rely on sensors to detect the initial stimulus and then transfer of the signal, with nervous signals being relayed much faster than hormones, which are released into the blood to be transported to their target organs and tissues. As a result both systems mean that animals are able to regulate their metabolism effectively and also respond and interact with their environment, with both hormones and nervous control playing essential roles.

5. *Where is testosterone found in a cat?*

This is a good question to test both your knowledge and ability to think carefully about your answer before diving in with it. The automatic, instinctive reply is "in the testicles," but after pausing for a moment you will then remember that a small proportion of testosterone is also produced by the adrenal glands, which sit just behind the kidneys. If you wanted to be especially clever and answer the question exactly right then you could add that it is found in the blood, as it is transported via the bloodstream – then again, this might be construed as being a bit cocky!

6. *What is a stem cell?*

A stem cell is a cell that, if given the correct signals and conditions, is capable of differentiating and developing into any type of tissue – it is pleuripotent. All organisms start life as a collection of stem cells, with different organs and anatomical features then developing from undifferentiated cells. The possibility of being able to understand and therefore control the behaviour of stem cells holds great promise for medicine, with the prospect of being able to regenerate damaged and aged tissue a very exciting and real one for the future. Imagine being able to grow new organs to use in transplants, with these being derived from a patient's very own stem cells and so having much less risk of being rejected? Or perhaps producing new retinal cells to restore sight to the blind? The possibilities are literally endless and there is a huge amount of scientific work being undertaken in this field.

7. *What was Louis Pasteur famous for? Why is it important?*

The second part of this question relies on you knowing the answer to the first but hopefully most people will have heard of Louis Pasteur and recognise the name of the process for which he is so famous: pasteurisation. This is something we are most familiar with when thinking about milk but is also applied to lots of other food stuffs to reduce the microbial load and therefore lengthen the shelf-life and safety, assuming that the product is then stored appropriately. Standard pasteurisation involves heating the substance being treated to a high temperature, but below boiling point to avoid denaturing the proteins. The aim is to reduce the number of pathogenic micro-organisms in food to levels that will not cause disease, rather than completely sterilise the substance.

Thought-provoking Questions

These are questions which don't necessarily have a correct answer but which ask you to think logically and apply your current knowledge and experiences, not only of veterinary but also of life in general, in discussing them. Interviewers will be interested in how you think, how you reason and explain your answers and whether you are able to think beyond the box in suggesting solutions to problems.

1. *Do you think the PDSA is good? Do you think they have any restrictions?*

No interviewer is suggesting for a second that the PDSA is not a good thing; on the contrary, most veterinarians would agree that the charities that provide assistance to people on low incomes to enable them to own and care properly for their pets are excellent in principle. What this question invites candidates to do is to consider the concept of there being pros and cons to everything and to form a reasoned and well-balanced personal opinion. For example, one benefit of such organizations is that they provide free of charge or subsidized preventative healthcare, such as vaccination, which helps to reduce the risk of certain diseases spreading within the pet population. However, others argue that there are limitations to these organizations and that providing free veterinary care gives people a distorted impression of the true cost of caring properly for an animal and that some people wrongly consider a pet as being a right, for which someone else should pay, rather than a privilege. There are many more similar arguments both for and against and I'm sure you can have fun debating them yourself.

2. *What is the biggest breakthrough in your opinion in the vet industry in the past 100 years?*

Again, there is no right or wrong answer. If you can justify your ideas then the interview panel will be impressed by your ability to reason an argument and answer a question to which you can't really 'swot up on.'

It is possible to take a number of completely different approaches, each being as impressive as one another. The most obvious answers will, of course, focus on major breakthroughs and there really is no shortage of such advances to choose from. Examples include the first use of ether to induce anaesthesia in 1846, making the practice of surgery more humane, through to Lister's 1867 principles of asepsis which dramatically help reduce surgical mortality, to Röentgen's discovery of X-rays in 1895. The last 100 years saw Fleming's discovery of penicillin and the birth of antibiotics, the development of vaccines and mass inoculation drives, dramatically reducing the prevalence of such awful diseases as distemper, and advances in welfare such as the development of the 'Five Freedoms.' There is probably no need for you to be able

from hunger & thirst
discomfort'
pain, injury or disease
to express normal behaviour
fear and distress

to quote the names of the vets and scientists who are credited with the breakthroughs but you should have a general idea of why they had such a huge impact.

The other way to answer this question, particularly if you are a budding surgeon, is turn the question on its head and show how little has changed in the last hundred years in many fields. If you visit the museums in the Royal College of Veterinary Surgeons in London and Surgeon's Hall in Edinburgh, one of the most striking things that you will see is how similar many of the surgical instruments of 150 years ago are to those used today. Of course our instruments today may be made out of plastic rather than carved from ivory and they may all be disposable rather than being handed down through the generations, but the form of the instruments and the principles of surgery have undergone more of a gradual evolution than a major leap forwards. Having said this, the pace of change in veterinary surgery even in the past 50 years has been staggering!

3. *Why do you think some vets find the profession difficult? What are the negative parts of the job? Do you think you would be able to cope with these?*

This question should be easy if you have done a decent amount of work-experience and actually taken the time and effort to speak with vets, farmers, nurses and all the other people you will have come into contact with. The reason most vets find the profession difficult is that they were not completely prepared for what lay in store for them on graduation. If you ensure that you go into the profession and your training with your eyes fully opened to both the positives and the negatives of being a vet – we have already discussed these in earlier chapters – then you will find it much easier to cope with the very real challenges that accompany being a veterinary professional. The key to this question is to be honest about the negative aspects of the career as you have experienced them, such as the high levels of stress and the fact that vets are not as well paid as their medical, dental or legal peers despite having as technically difficult a job and working hours which are often comparable or longer. You then want to finish by briefly identifying the positive personal traits that you have and how these prove your ability to cope with the stresses and challenges of being a vet. Simply answering the last part of this question with an unqualified "yeah, I would," will not impress anyone. They want to hear examples of stressful and challenging situations you have dealt with and to see that you have the potential to really make it through the course and become a happy member of the profession. *Being an au pair in Brussels.*

4. *Imagine the following situation. I walk into your surgery with my dog and after examining it you realize there is something seriously wrong and you need to perform surgery. How would you approach me to tell me this?*

Would you just come out with it and tell the owner that their dog has a serious problem? Probably not. A good clinician, and communicator, would let the owner know the seriousness of the situation by using a carefully coordinated series of non-verbal and verbal communication techniques. For example, inviting the owner to take a seat before telling them what is wrong will mentally prepare the owner for potentially bad news, as will adopting a somber, serious tone and manner, as opposed to being jocular and smiley. In terms of the words you would use, it is important to explain the problem to the owner in language that they will understand rather than charging in with a description of how their dog has "a gastric torsion with evidence of acidosis." They would probably just stare at you blankly and may even get agitated at you for your inability to explain things to them clearly. They will want you, as the vet, to be empathetic, and acknowledge their concern, but to also be authoritative and knowledgeable. They will expect you to offer them options, discuss the risks and costs and to guide, rather than dictate, the owner towards the best option for both the owner and, most importantly, their dog.

5. *How would the above situation differ if I brought along my five year old son who was very attached to this dog?*

You might sensitively suggest to the parent that they take their child out of the room whilst you have a quiet word with them, and then maybe offer to explain things to their son (assuming you have an ability to converse with children – many people don't). Most parents will want to have the situation explained carefully to them and then they will normally explain to their children what the problem is.

> **6.** *I can see you do a lot outside of school. What would you want to be doing if you came here?*

This question does several things. First, it is drawing attention to the fact that you have a lot of extra-curricular activities and the panel may ask to hear more about how you organize your time to fit them in around your schoolwork and work-experience. It is also a great opportunity to show how much you know about the university you are interviewing at, as you will have read the prospectus and have a good idea of what activities, for example sports, are on offer at the uni.

Ethical Questions

These are some of the hardest questions to answer as they are often controversial in their very nature. As with the other challenging and probing questions they do not have a right or a wrong answer but rather test your ability to reason, discuss and form your own balanced opinion on a range of issues. Being asked this type of question is a positive sign as it shows that the interview panel want to stretch you and really see what you're made of – they would only do this if you were a serious contender for an offer.

1. *What do you see as being the main issues with regard to using animals in scientific research and teaching?*

The general publics' opinion on this subject is unsurprisingly going to vary wildly, from those who are indifferent to those who vehemently oppose any use of animals in any capacity. As a prospective vet it is important for you to be aware of the fact that animal testing happens and to understand the reasons for this. At present no new drug can be licensed, either for veterinary or medical use, without having first undergone stringent testing on animals. Much of our current knowledge of the basic sciences and medicine has arisen as a direct result of work carried out using animals. It is important to point out the fact that all research carried out using laboratory animals is closely monitored and scrutinized by the Home Office, and experiments must receive approval before they can be carried out. The animals involved, of which the vast majority in research are mice, are cared for by highly skilled teams of technicians and vets and not exposed to any undue suffering. Laboratory animals are kept in conditions that would probably make most domestic pets envious!

Although the use of animals in research is still essential there are always efforts being made to reduce our need for them, and any good scientist, when designing an experiment and planning research, will explore the various options open to them. There is a guiding principle when considering these issues and this is the 'Three Rs': Reduce, Refine and Replace. Is it possible to reduce the number of animals needed for a particular experiment, for example by employing computer simulation? Are there ways in which the experiment could be designed to yield high quality results whilst managing to reduce the degree of suffering imposed or the number of test subjects required? Are there other ways to obtain the results that we are interested in that doesn't involve animal use? Computer modeling is an area that is developing well and will continue to be an important tool in research.

Veterinary teaching requires animals, from the use of fresh and fixed cadavers in dissection classes, which are essential in teaching future vets anatomy and helping to develop fundamental surgical skills, to microscope slides of healthy and diseased tissues and handling classes with live animals, to teach students the basics of key skills such as bandaging. Although there are many aspects of teaching that we are now able to use technology to demonstrate, such as the 'Haptic Cow', which provides students with a simulated experience of pregnancy diagnosis by rectal palpation in cows, there is still the need to use animals in the education of our future vets and this is something that you need to be both aware and accepting of. In short, there is no time for someone on the course who has extreme views on the use of animals for learning, and if you do feel that this will be an issue then I suggest you either learn more about veterinary and what the teaching and profession involve or look at alternative career options.

2. *What are your thoughts on rearing animals for meat?*

Whether you are a committed vegetarian or not, and many vets are, you must be accepting of the fact that vets play a vital role in the meat industry, from ensuring the welfare of animals transported to and held at abattoirs to inspection of carcasses and, ultimately, the safeguarding of public health. Vet students are required to spend time seeing practice in an abattoir and are lectured on all aspects of large animal practice. There is no option for opting out of this training and even if you never plan to handle another production animal again post-graduation, as a vet you have a duty and obligation to complete training and achieve competency in all aspects of veterinary.

3. *Do you think that all badgers should be killed because of the TB outbreak?*

Before you would be able to even attempt to answer this question and offer an opinion it is vital that you have some background knowledge of bovine tuberculosis (bTB) and why it is so important in UK farming.

Tuberculosis (TB) is an important disease in cattle and is a potential zoonosis, with cases occasionally seen in those working closely with cattle, such as farm and abattoir workers, and immune-suppressed individuals. The disease in cattle is caused by a bacterium, Mycobacterium bovis, and the disease normally leads to coughing, weight loss and, occasionally, diarrhoea, with skin and mammary forms also possible. The detection, monitoring, prevention, research and compensation associated with TB costs UK taxpayers approximately £100 million per year and is therefore a huge economic burden.

Pasteurisation of milk has greatly reduced the number of cases and decreased infections by 99% since the 1950s, when there were an average of 2,500 deaths from TB per year.

The main method of screening for TB in cattle is the 'tuberculin skin test.' You may have seen this being done when you were on large animal practice. Two small injections are given under the skin on the neck, each containing a protein called tuberculin, with one extracted from M.bovis and the other from M.avium (the bird form of the disease), which is used as a reference point for the reaction. All herds in the South of England and Wales, where TB is a major issue, are currently tested at least once every twelve months. The tuberculin injections are administered on a clipped area of skin on the neck and the skin thickness measured with calipers both before and 72 hours after the injections are given. If the thickness of the M.bovis site is a certain amount greater than that of the M.avium one then the cow may be identified either as an 'inconclusive reactor (IR)' or as a reactor.

IRs are those animals where the response falls within a grey area and in these cases the farm is initially put on standard movement restrictions, with no movement of cattle permitted off the farm, although these are normally lifted as long as the IR is isolated and retested 60 days later, assuming there are no other reactors in the herd. Herds with reactors are placed on restriction and cannot move cattle from the farm unless a special slaughter license is granted and the animal(s) in question are sent to an abattoir which is able to accept stock from TB herds. These herds are re-tested every 60days until there are no reactors for two consecutive tests. Cattle that test positive for TB or are identified as IRs twice are required to be culled by Animal Health, the government agency in charge of controlling TB. One issue with testing is that there is no such thing as a perfect one. The tuberculin skin test has high specificity (99%), meaning that if there is a reaction then there is a very high chance that TB is present. The problem is that it has a relatively low sensitivity so can't always be relied on to detect cases that exist. There is a blood test available, the gamma-interferon test, which is routinely used in other countries and can be used in conjunction with the tuberculin test. The blood test, however, has the opposite problem as it is possible to get false positives.

It is accepted that badgers are implicated in the spread of bovine tuberculosis, with a proven high prevalence of the disease in areas with large badger populations. There was a large scale badger cull planned for Wales with the intention being to then vaccinate all other badgers in the UK. This has, however, been postponed after being challenged in the courts so at the time of writing it is not clear what the future is with regard to the role of badgers in the spread of TB, although new plans for a cull in parts of Wales are being suggested. Farmers are able to take practical steps to decrease the risk of spread to their cattle by reducing the attractiveness of their farm to badgers. It is important to store cattle feed securely and to be aware of where active sets and badger latrines are, with the aim then being to keep cattle away from these areas. Care must also be taken when buying in new stock and the TB status of the source herd should be ascertained.

The question itself asks specifically about whether all badgers should be killed due to the TB outbreak. As with any such question there are several sides of the argument, both for and against, and it is important to present all of these before arriving at your own, informed personal opinion. The Krebs Review, which was a large study into the relationship between badgers and the spread of TB, looked at the effect on the prevalence of TB of culling badgers in certain areas. The results were surprising and showed that culling resulted in a decrease in TB in that area but a concurrent increase was then seen in adjoining areas. This may have been due to migration of TB infected badgers from one area into others. The argument, therefore, is that culling only works if done on a huge scale such that all TB-infected badgers are killed. This would not only be logistically difficult and costly but any culling programme is always divisive politically and many people are fundamentally opposed to the principle of killing one of our much-loved native species, especially when they feel that it is being done principally for economic reasons. You are obviously entitled to your own opinion as long as you can justify it.

4. *What would you say is an important welfare issue at the moment?*

There are a number of potential examples of topical welfare issues which may prove fertile ground for debate, especially if you have been able to do a bit of background research on the subjects. These include:

- Pedigree dogs and the effects on welfare of exaggerated physical features and inherited diseases.

- Religious slaughter and the exemption for slaughter without pre-stunning.

- Battery hens and Broilers. *No more caged eggs by 2025*

- Dangerous dogs and legislation governing them, especially in light of evidence suggesting an increase in incidents of dog-fighting and the use of dogs as weapons.

- The increased 'industrialisation' of dairy farming and the production pressures placed on UK dairy cattle.

There are so many possible topics that could be debated in an animal welfare context and I am sure you can think of several yourself.

Current Affairs

Keeping an eye on the press, both veterinary and general, is a good idea in the months leading up to your interview as there is a very good chance that you'll be asked a question either directly linked to, or certainly influenced by, events of veterinary importance. There is no expectation that you will be an expert – after all, you have far too much on your plate with gaining work-experience, studying hard and engaging in extra-curricular activities without finding the time to trawl through every reference and report on subjects of veterinary interest. Being aware of issues and having some basic grasp of the facts will be sufficient to enable you to answer questions and engage in debate with the interviewers.

1. *What can you tell me about emerging diseases in animals and PETS?*

With greater numbers of people taking their pets with them on holiday, coupled with continuing climate change, it was only a matter of time before we started to see the emergence of new diseases to the UK. When we say 'new diseases' what we mean are diseases that have never been seen in UK animals before. This is an area of real concern and one which efforts are directed at halting. One example of such a disease is that caused by the parasite Angiostrongylus vasorum, or the French heartworm. The adults live in the right ventricle (one of the chambers of the heart) and the pulmonary arteries (those entering the lungs from the heart). They lay eggs, which hatch very quickly, and the larvae then cross the alveoli of the lungs before being coughed up and swallowed. They are then passed through the gut and eliminated in the faeces. In order to develop completely, the larvae need to spend time in an intermediate host, choosing either slugs or snails. If a dog eats an infected slug or snail, or even comes into contact with the infected slime trail left by them on things like water bowls or toys left in the garden, the worms enter the dog and travel to the heart, where the cycle is then repeated. In areas where lungworm is endemic, foxes are known to act as a reservoir for infection.

As you would imagine, the clinical signs associated with this parasite are related to the location that the adult worms live within the dog and include signs such as difficulties breathing (dyspnoea), caused by lung damage, and coughing, including that of blood (haemoptysis). A reduction in the flow of blood to the lungs from the blocked right ventricle can also lead to lethargy and fainting. Lungworm can also affect normal blood clotting, which may then result in excessive bruising, bleeding disorders, including increased bleeding times and risk of haemorrhage during surgery, and neurological symptoms if a bleed occurs within the central nervous system. Other associated signs can include poor growth, lameness, diarrhoea and blindness. A lot of these signs may easily be explained by other, more commonly seen, conditions and so it is possible that lungworm is under-diagnosed in the UK.

Treatment can be tricky as dogs may suffer an allergic reaction to the dead and dying worms whilst they are still in the body. Infected animals may require adjunctive treatment and support, such as antibiotics and oxygen supplementation, during treatment with an effective anthelmintic. It is possible to treat pets regularly against lungworm as part of their routine worming regime, and this is something that I personally advise all of our dog owners to do.

A.vasorum is a prime example of one of the many diseases and parasites that are not normally seen in the UK and which vets and authorities are worried will be seen more frequently as a result of travel and climate change, enabling these conditions to be introduced and to then thrive here. The pet travel scheme (PETS), which issues passports to pets travelling to various parts of the world, is intended to dramatically reduce the risk of such diseases being introduced into the UK. There is more information on PETS to follow.

Other examples of important diseases to be aware of that may be introduced to the UK by pets travelling back into the UK are:

1. **Rabies** – this viral disease is endemic in many European countries and is one that all pets wishing to re-enter the UK must be vaccinated against. If they are not vaccinated

or do not have a valid passport then animals have to spend six months in quarantine to monitor them for any development of the disease, before they can be released.

2. **Leishmaniasis** – this protozoal disease, which is spread by biting sandflies, is endemic in a number of Mediterranean countries. The parasite enters the bloodstream by infecting macrophages (a type of white blood cell) and can then spread to various organs in the body, including the skin, where it causes a range of symptoms. Any animal presented to a vet with suspected infectious disease and with a history of prior travel, even if it was several years ago, should include Leishmaniasis on the list of differential diagnoses. The most effective way to protect pets from this parasite is to avoid being bitten by sandflies. This is achieved by minimizing time spent in areas with sandflies, especially at dusk when they tend to be at their most active, and by treating pets with an effective insecticide.

3. **_Echinococcus multiocularis_** – this is a tapeworm which is contracted when dogs and cats eat infected meat. It causes relatively little disease in both dogs and cats, who are examples of definitive hosts, and attaches to the gut lining, where they produce eggs. If these eggs, which are present in the animal's faeces, are accidentally eaten by an intermediate host, including humans, then they can cause something known as 'hydatid disease.' E. multiocularis invades the bloodstream and travels to the

liver where cysts are formed. They can also spread to other organs, including the brain, where the cysts grow and invade surrounding tissue, resembling a highly invasive and aggressive cancer. It is, therefore, a very important example of a zoonosis and one to be taken seriously. It is important to treat pets regularly with an anthelmintic (wormer) which is effective against this tapeworm.

A zoonosis is a disease which normally infects animals but which can also infect humans. They are therefore of great importance and great efforts are directed towards studying them and protecting humans from their effects. Vets play an incredibly important role in this ongoing battle.

PETS (Pet Travel Scheme)

This was established in 2000 originally for dogs and cats travelling into the UK from certain EU countries. It was later extended to include several other countries, including some non-EU such as mainland USA, Canada and Bahrain, and also to cover pet ferrets. The purpose of PETS is principally to protect the UK from the introduction of rabies and other specific diseases. Dogs, cats and ferrets travelling back to the UK under PETS need to satisfy certain requirements in order to avoid having to spend time in quarantine:

1. Animals must be microchipped before any other stage of the process is completed and the number clearly recorded. The microchip must be easily found when the animal is scanned.

2. All dogs, cats and ferrets entering the UK must be vaccinated against rabies. This can be done once the animal has been microchipped so that they can be easily identified. Some vets recommend a booster rabies injection two weeks after the first, especially if it is the first time they have been vaccinated against the disease, to increase the chances of stimulating a good level of immunity.

3. An authorized veterinary surgeon is then able to issue a pet passport. It used to be the case that a blood test was required to demonstrate adequate levels of antibodies to rabies before a passport could be issued, but this was changed a couple of years ago so that all that is required now is rabies vaccination alone.

Rabies vaccination needs to be boosted according to the specific advice given on the vaccine manufacturer's datasheet and it is vital to keep animals up to date. Pets may leave the UK as soon as they have been vaccinated against rabies but cannot reenter the country if less that 21 days has lapsed since their last vaccination.

Haven't build a strong enough immunity up yet.

4. Treatment against tapeworm has to be given to pets 24 to 48 hours before re-entering the UK. This needs to be completed by and certified by a vet. Tick treatment is no longer compulsory, but is strongly recommended by vets.

5. Animals must travel with an approved transport company and on an authorized route.

It is important to note that it is ultimately the owner's responsibility to check the specific requirements for travel of their own pet and to ensure that all paperwork is up to date.

For more detailed information on PETS go to the DEFRA website (www.defra.gov.uk).

2. What is your opinion of veterinary TV programmes?

Vets have always been an attractive prospect for TV producers as the work we are engaged in is, on the whole, engaging, interesting and when it comes to animals, the UK is undoubtedly one of the most besotted nations on the planet! We love watching anything medical on television and if it happens to include cute animals as well then this makes an already interesting show un-missable. Series focusing on the work of vets have included Super Vets, which followed the work of referral vets at The Royal Veterinary College in London, and The Bionic Vet, which focused on the pioneering work of orthopaedic specialist Noel Fitzpatrick and his team. Although no-one would deny that these programmes dramatically raise the profile of the profession and offer the general public a fascinating insight into the work of modern vets, whilst being gripping, dramatic and, to be honest, thoroughly entertaining, they do raise a few questions.

The first point to make is that recent veterinary series have focused very much on the work of referral, or specialist, vets and so may be at risk of distorting the general public's impression of what vets can do in everyday practice. One danger is that client expectations may be unrealistically raised with regard to what treatments are able to be offered by their local vets and this can lead to difficulties when approaching a case in a logical, first-opinion manner. What do you say to a client whose dog needs a cruciate ligament repair but who wants some fancy new procedure that they saw on TV? The programme itself will probably have focused on how well the surgery went and how much of an improvement the patient has made, all condensed into a few short minutes of cleverly edited and sound-engineered footage, which would have most people demanding the same for their own pets. What the programmes will usually neglect to highlight, mainly because it would take too long and is, quite frankly, dull, is the need to carefully consider the pros and cons of all available procedures and treatments, the risks of secondary infection and complications and the resulting treatment of said complications, which may dramatically extend the recovery time and eventual outcome of the treatment option selected. Simply focusing the viewer's mind on the before and (final) after pictures may distort the real story.

The second, related, point to make is that these recent shows have focused very much on the cutting edge, specialist side of veterinary, which actually accounts for a very small proportion of the work carried out by members of the profession. Graduates and prospective vets watching these shows may be led to believe that what they are watching on TV is broadly representative of the type of work they will expect to be doing whilst at vet school and following graduation. What they don't, however, highlight is the fact that approximately 80% of new graduates enter first-opinion practice after university and a lot of their working lives will be spent engaged in the less glamorous aspects of the job, such as administering vaccinations, expressing anal glands and performing routine elective surgeries such as neutering. Of course there are opportunities to then progress your career by specialising, either by undertaking certificates or completing internships and residencies, but these require many additional years of hard work, and potentially a drop in earnings, before achieving. This makes it even more vitally important for you to undertake work-experience so that you can actually see what most vets do, rather than be given the false impression that we're all engaged in high level specialist work. By all means aspire to emulate the fantastic vets we see in such shows but do so fully aware of the fact that doing so is no easy feat and will require 100% commitment and a lot of very hard work.

Another observation to make is that the veterinary work that such programmes focus on tends to encourage prospective vets into areas of practice where we are, perhaps, over-subscribed and well-staffed. The types of vet that we do need more of in the UK include farm animal vets, with no primetime show yet following the working life of these professionals. Granted, there are shows which spend time shadowing vets dealing with large animals but these are predominantly zoo vets or those working in exciting parts of the world and with unusual animals, such as in Africa. There are, of course, vets employed in these fields but, again, not giving any airtime to 'regular' farm vets is giving a skewed view of the profession and what one can realistically expect from entering it. The danger, if this isn't realised at any early stage, is that new graduates leave university disillusioned and disgruntled with the result being that they either remain in practice feeling perpetually unfulfilled and regretful of the decisions they made, or they leave the profession, which seems like such an awful waste of the skills and training that they will possess and which have been invested in them.

What happens after Interview?

After you've been interviewed, the process of waiting begins. This can be a stressful period as you dwell on the interviews you've already had whilst worrying about upcoming ones, all while continuing to juggle your studies and extra-curricular commitments. As difficult as it is to do it really is a good idea to try and put previous interviews behind you. They are in the past and there is nothing you are going to be able to do now that will change the outcome. By all means learn lessons from them and if there are certain questions that you know you could have answered better or you feel your interview style wasn't quite as polished as it could be then work on improving for the next interview, assuming that you have one coming up. Interviews, like exams, are strange beasts to call and often pointless to do so. My Bristol interview was, in my mind, an absolute disaster as I answered questions incorrectly and felt myself getting stressed and flustered. I was so convinced that I had mucked it up that I went straight home to start furiously preparing for my London one. I did, however, then get an offer so it just goes to show that just because we may have felt things went badly, the chances are that your interview did, in actual fact, go well and you're in line to receive an offer.

It is rare to be called back for an additional interview and the most likely thing to happen after your interview is to receive an email from UCAS to say whether you have an offer (either conditional on certain grades being achieved, or unconditional), have been placed on to a 'reserve list' (so there is still hope of a place), or been rejected. The last result is understandably gutting but don't let it put you off preparing well for any upcoming interviews – if anything, let it spur you on to be even more awesome so the vet school can't possibly refuse you! You can track your applications on the UCAS website and respond to any offers you receive. Some vet schools may contact you directly to make an offer. One student I know received a phone call from Professor Gary England, head of Nottingham Vet

School, to say that she had been accepted – a great telephone call to get!

All that's left to do after hearing from the vet schools is to knuckle down and make sure you nail the exams and get top grades. Even if you are rejected from all of your choices I still strongly advise putting your all in for your exams – you may be lucky and be able to approach the vet schools on results day with a fantastic set of results and still secure an offer. Besides, even if you don't make it to vet school then a top set of grades will make it more likely that you will second time around, if reapplying, or open up many other doors if you choose to tread a slightly different career path.

What if I don't get any offers?

Try and keep your chin up and remember that life will go on and you will do well. If phoning the vet schools on results day to make one final check whether they will accept you or not is unsuccessful then the choices you have are the following:

1. Take a Gap Year and reapply next year, this time with a top set of grades firmly under your belt, and loads more relevant and interesting work-experience to write and talk about. If you don't have any success the second time around then I would strongly discourage you making a third attempt and would, instead, suggest taking one of the alternative routes below.

2. Consider applying to study veterinary in another country. It is, obviously, going to be a much more expensive option and involve a lot more organisation and upheaval compared to studying in the UK but if you really can't bear the thought of not being a vet, you and your family can realistically afford it and you relish the challenge of living and studying abroad then go for it. You can find further information on applying on the individual vet schools' websites.

3. Accept the offer from your 'insurance' course, assuming you both applied to one and received an offer, and study at university for a degree in a different subject. Whether you then opt to apply to vet school as a graduate or follow a different career path is then your prerogative. Many excellent vets have come onto the course as graduates, and there are a number of specific benefits of being one, whilst other people I know studied different subjects, not even necessarily scientific or with any direct veterinary relevance, and followed varied and interesting careers with absolutely no feelings of regret. Life is a strange journey and sometimes the path which you find yourself on, despite not being the one originally on your planned map, turns out to be the best for you in the long-run. Deep but true.

4. Take a break from studying and reassess your options. This may involve entering the world of work, travelling, volunteering or whatever else you want to do. Sometimes, simply taking time to reflect and take stock of things is all that's needed for everything to become clear again.

SUMMARY

Interviews at vet school should be seen as yet another important door through which you have to walk in order to achieve your ultimate goal of a place at university to study veterinary. Each vet school has their own unique approach to them, some more unique and individual than others, but they can , and should, be prepared for. Even being invited to a vet school interview is a huge achievement in itself and should be celebrated.

Jemima Mead

BVetMed(Hons) MRCVS ACIM

Brand Manager, Small Animals
Sales & Marketing, Boehringer
Ingelheim, Companion Animal
Health

Hi my name is Jemima Mead. I graduated from the Royal Veterinary College in London in 2006. After 4 years working in general practice I moved into veterinary industry and now work for one of the top 20 pharmaceutical companies in the world. I am responsible for managing our portfolio of cardiology products for dogs throughout the UK and the Republic of Ireland. It is a busy job which combines the science of vet school, my knowledge of working life as a vet as well as my more creative side! When I am not working I love spending time walking, running and cycling on the South Downs in West Sussex where I live with my husband and our two cats (British shorthairs called Teddy and Beatrice). I hope you find this glimpse into my career useful, it goes to show that a veterinary degree opens may doors behind which lie new and exciting challenges!

Industry Vet

1. When did you decide you wanted to be a vet?

I first decided I wanted to be a vet following work experience at the age of 15, whilst at school in London. I went to a girl's school and most of the other pupils wanted to be solicitors or the like so were organising placements in places such as law firms. No one at my school had ever qualified as a vet and so the whole experience was new and guidance on how to get into vet school was limited. I arranged a placement with a small animal clinic in Putney and absolutely loved it, returning to work on Saturdays for them where I remained until I did my A-levels. The clinic had two vets and had a particular interest in spinal surgery. They were incredibly enthusiastic and caring, and the whole place had a great atmosphere. I could really picture myself doing everything that they were doing.

I had grown up around animals but never really had a fluffy idea about being a vet, in terms of getting to sit around all day stroking cute animals. As a pupil I enjoyed maths and science and at the vets was just happy to get involved with everything they did. I had previously flirted with the idea of doing other things, such as being a solicitor, but really had my sights set firmly on becoming a vet. When I was 17 the programme "Vet School", based at Bristol university then came out, although by that point I had decided on my career direction. I was the last year to be able to apply to all of the vet schools and started at the Royal Veterinary College, London, in 2001 after taking a Gap Year, during which I worked, travelled and generally enjoyed having some time away from academia.

2. What was your experience of organising work experience placements whilst applying?

Small animal and equine placements were relatively straightforward to arrange in and around London, although finding farm practice was a little trickier. Helpfully, a girl at school had an uncle with a farm in Penrith so I was able to spend time there doing various things, including lambing and dairy work.

3. Why did you want to be a vet?

There were probably two main reasons. First was that I always liked, and do like, a challenge, being quite analytical and intrigued by how things work. The second was that I wanted to make a difference, and to improve lives but not just in the soft, fluffy manner. It was great to be able to see animals and their owners being made better.

I was incredibly proud of being offered a place at vet school but didnt apply just because it was tough to apply, which may be an attraction to some. At the time I always envisioned myself working in small animal practice and never once thought that I would not be in practice.

4. What were the highlights of vet school for you?

There were many highlights, from the people I met and the friendships that I made from day one, to EMS, which was hard work but good fun. There is a motto at vet school - "work hard; play hard" - and this was certainly true at London. There was a great sense of comararderie and a really positive, bubbly atmosphere, which has the overall effect of being really fun. From sports days on Wednesday afternoons, to some amazing parties, such as the annual May ball, I had a great time. The only downside to being so close-knit is that everyone ends up knowing your business and I was proactive in ensuring that I had a life outside of the immediate vet school one that I had, especially as I had friends and family already in London. The vet world can feel like a very small one and it is easy to feel as though you have no breathing space.

The course was incredibly busy, which does make it very difficult to have a part-time job and earn extra money. The first year was tough, with lots of basic sciences, resulting in us feeling as though we were repeating a lot of what we had covered at A-level, which was a bit of a hard slog. However, when we got the chance to do more clinical activities then it was great.

5. **What were the main challenges of vet school for you?**

Having little to no money! No-one ever talks about how to survive at university without much money, or how to budget, or even how to manage your time effectively. I did actually manage to have a part-time job whilst at vet school, which did help. Another challenge was taking ownership of my own learning, as we're encouraged to do, as it is very important to balance academic work, relaxing, building personal relationships, and also doing things outside of the veterinary degree. I probably did a little too much extra learning and work in my first year in hindsight.

6. How aware were you of 'industry' during your time at vet school?

I wasn't really aware of what being a vet in industry entailed until my fifth, and final, year. We had a careers day with various vets who came in to talk about their careers. We had some small animal surgeons from the Queen Mother's Hospital, talking about internships and residencies; a meat hygiene inspector; a practice owner; and a technical vet from a veterinary pharmaceutical company, who I remember listening to and instantly switching off. I had always wanted to do a residency and already had a small animal job agreed for graduation. My plan at that stage was to do two years in practice before going on and completing a residency to become a surgeon.

7. When and why did you decide to move into a more commercial role?

I first started to have thoughts of a change after about two years in practice. There were a number of factors that led to me ultimately deciding against a residency: I met my now husband; I enjoyed earning relatively good money, as opposed to the option of going back to earning very little; I was, at the time, on a 1 in 10 on-call rota and certainly didn't fancy going to a 1 in 2; and I didn't want to be treated like a dogsbody, which unfortunately was the impression given from a lot of those on internships and residencies.

I worked in Hertfordshire for 18 months and then moved to West Sussex as my husband was going to buy into a practice there (he's also a vet). I locumed in a 4-vet practice for a a few months but missed working as part of a large team, and so considered my options. I moved across to Chichester and worked in an 8-10 vet practice for a couple of years where I started to see some of the difficulties associated with either doing an advanced certificate or even having kids whilst still working in general practice. I was also at a stage where I wanted a new challenge and to have new opportunities in my career so I started looking at industry roles, initially at technical positions, as I wasn't aware that there were any other options for vets. A few friends of mine had moved into industry and were either in technical or regulatory roles, neither of which were quite right for me. One day I went into the pharmacy in my practice and looked at who made all the products. Following this I started looking into the various companies and spoke to friends about their companies and their culture. I found myself very much drawn towards Boehringer Ingelheim due to a good feeling I was getting about their company culture.

In January 2010 I felt that things were not as good as they could be for me at work and was having a look in the veterinary press where I saw my current job being advertised. The closing date for applications was that day so I didn't have time to apply but thought that I would if a similar role came up. It then played on my mind all week so I called the Vet Record, where I had seen the advert, and asked if I could request a pdf of the original advert, which I was fortunate enough to receive. I then called the recruitment consultant and enquired about whether I would still be able to apply, even though I acknowledged the closing date had passed. I was told that if I was able to submit my CV and a covering letter by the following day then I would be considered. With a lot of hard work and steely determination that is exactly what I did.

There were three stages to the recruitment process, with the first being an interview with the recruitment consultant, then another, this time with my now boss also being present. The third stage was held at head office, where we were interviewed further and given psychometric tests to complete and presentations to deliver. The entire process took approximately 6-8 weeks and with long reflection periods (about 3 weeks) between each stage and a big investment asked in terms of time and effort, it really made me reflect on whether I really was sure that I wanted the job, which of course I did. I was finally given the job on the 6th April 2010, which coincided exactly with BSAVA (British Small Animal Veterinary Association) Congress, one of our biggest events of the year, and so I was very much thrown in at the deep end (which I loved).

8. **What is your current role?**

My role at present is Brand Manager, with responsibility for complete management of a portfolio of cardiac products for dogs. This is the job that I was originally hired to do and during my time in the role I have achieved much, from completing a professional diploma in marketing, which BI paid for and supported me through, to developing other skills, including more advanced IT expertise, especially in programmes such as Excel and some powerful data analysis software. The level of ongoing support and training that I receive from the company is exceptional with the company being incredibly supportive of employee development. We have development plans each year, which are reviewed every six months, and get the chance to complete various courses to further develop our relevant skills.

9. What are your key responsibilities and what do you do on a day to day basis?

My working life sees me doing lots of different things and working with many different people including other vets within our technical teams, financial controllers, our sales force and creative agencies. I am responsible for developing the marketing campaigns part of which involves designing initiatives for our sales force to use with vets in practice. I spend a lot of time talking to and visiting members of the sales force to see how well the initiatives are being implemented. These visits are also an important opportunity to take the pulse of the market and understand the pressures, changes and opportunities available to us.

I also work on more long-term strategy planning, such as product life-cycle management, and travel internationally on a regular basis, on average once per month, although it varies depending on exactly what I am working on at the time. For example, I visit our headquarters in Ingelheim, Germany, four to five times per year, and have been to Dubai recently, as well as attending a number of international conferences. My job sees me working a lot with veterinary specialists, with visits to various universities and centres of excellence being required. There is a lot of relationship building that comes with the role and so I often attend big conferences and smaller, more specialist subject-specific conferences, especially those with a cardiac focus.

As aluded to earlier, I am responsible for our cardiac products in the UK, including stock control and logistics. In other words, it is my responsibility to ensure we always have sufficient stock to supply the market. I also work closely with our regulatory team on matters of compliance and even on changes, such as packaging alterations. All in all, I have a very pivotal and highly varied role – it is a job I thoroughly enjoy.

10. How have you found the transition from clinical practice to an industry role?

One of the biggest changes from working in practice is the time it takes to see an effect of the work you have done. As a vet you have a worried owner bring in their pet who has a problem, and within a relatively short period of time you work out what is going on and what you can do to help/resolve the situation. My job now is very much about longer term planning and change. A lot of what I do operates in cycles with the shortest cycle being 3-4 months and the longer ones 2-3 years. Therefore, you learn to be patient and a period of adaption is necessary to understand how well you are doing a job when the results or changes are not immediately obvious.

My current role has required a different set of skills to when I was in practice, although some are directly transferable, such as strong communication skills. It is more the industry knowledge and insight that has been the asset that I have brought to the role. Being a vet I understand the challenges related to the veterinary industry, and having a good idea of what it is that vets want, what information they need and how much time you can expect to command their attention, is what has really been key. Being able to put myself in the vets' position has helped to guide a lot of the initiatives I run. For example, knowing that vets would find a cardiac medication dosage chart in their room useful but wanting to avoid it being obvious to the client that they are having to look the dose up led us to design a series of mouse mats with the information on. As such, vets have the info they need at a glance and clients are none the wiser that they have looked it up. A very clever idea and one borne out of knowing what it's like to be a vet in practice (as well as canvassing opinion from my husband).

The various perks of the job have also helped make the transition a pleasant one, from being able to wear nice clothes to work without the worry of getting fur and other substances on them, to having a great car and working a far more civilised day, with no weekends. Well, there is usually one weekend a year that I have to do some work but that is it.

11. What has been your career highlight so far?

Without a doubt, it was winning the VMA (Veterinary Marketing Association) Young Marketer of the Year Award 2011, which was awarded in March 2012 at the annual dinner in London. It was amazing.

12. Where do you see yourself in 5 years? 10 years?

I can definately see myself still working with BI as I currently work in a company I love and with a fantastic team. The fact that they have been one of the Top 100 companies to work for every year for the past ten years says it all. There are so many career options available that it really is difficult to know where I will be in five years, let alone in ten. I can certainly see myself continuing to work in the UK and to have a family, but to keep working. I really love marketing and the culture here at BI is great. They are also a very ethical company that is focused on really making a difference and everyone is committed to improving lives of both animals and people, which is another strong reason why I chose BI.

13. **Do you miss any aspects of traditional clinical practice?**

No. I have no regrets and the best decision I made was to move into industry. I would say, however, that the best parts of practice for me were (some) clients, (some) of their pets, and surgery, especially feline and it is this which I would focus more on if I ever did clinical practice again. However, I wouldn't change what I do now and my work-life balance is significantly improved. Plus, I no longer dread the on-call phone going off!

14. **What advice would you offer anyone considering veterinary as a career option?**

I loved most of my career in clinical practice and veterinary medicine is a very rewarding career option. However, there are aspects of practice that no matter how well you prepare for them will never fully understand the realities until you do them for yourself. Dealing with financial constraints in life and death situations were some of the toughest aspects of practice. With that said, I wouldn't be doing what I am now if I hadn't gone to vet school, qualified as a vet and worked in clinical practice. It is a fantastic career to go into, not necessarily to be a clinician, as vets can and do turn their hands to many things.

I do think that money should be discussed more and the fact is that vets are never really paid well, not compared to other professions. I would advise getting as much experience as you can before vet school, both of practice and seeing what it is that this career can offer, and also of life in general. It is also very easy to become blinkered regarding your career and the options available. There is absolutely no shame either in admitting that what you're doing is no longer what you want to do. This should be discussed more and we should be more honest about various aspects of the profession with prospective applicants, including being honest about the high emotional strain that being a vet entails and the unfortunately high suicide rate, which is something that is never really talked about. I think it is very important that prospective applicants are really sure that being a vet is something that they truly want to do and commit to.

Also, be prepared for change and be open to other opportunities. It is very important to be aware of work-life balance and it is completely ok to look at and consider other options during your life and career.

VET SCHOOL

2: LIFE AT VET SCHOOL

All things being well you have received an offer, achieved the required grades and are now due to start university as a brand new vet student - pretty exciting, huh?! This is basically where the adventure really begins, as you make the transition from school pupil (unless you're reading this as a graduate, in which case you know what it is you're in for) to uni student. Chances are that you will already have some ideas about what life at university involves, some accurate and realistic, others based on far-fetched hearsay and popular media, such as films or TV shows. You may well know people at university already and so will have had a chance to speak with them about their experiences. If you haven't then its a great idea to find someone to have a chat with about being a student.

Although being a vet student is, in many ways a typical student experience, it is also different in many unique ways, in large part due to both the length of the course and the fact that the workload is so much greater than most other degrees. We will explore some of these unique aspects of vetdom in due course.

At this stage there will be lots of actions on your vet school "to do before starting uni list," including sorting out accommodation and finalising the matter of finances. Then, of course, there is the small matter of turning your mind towards the life-changing process of actually leaving home. For many of you this will be the first time you have spent any significant amount of time living away from home - a daunting but exhilarating prospect. Some of you may even be able to put such thoughts to the back of your mind for the time being as you contemplate plans for a Gap Year. If so then you might want to pop a bookmark in this page and come back in a few month's time. Those of you counting down the days until the 'big move,' read on....

What do I need to sort out before starting university?

The main things to sort out before actually, physically arriving to start vet school, are:

1. **Accommodation** - where are you going to live?

Most first years will have applied to and been offered a room in a student hall, or separate house owned by the university. There are several options and not every one of these is going to suit every student. The main types of first-year accommodation are:

Catered halls - these are usually large buildings with lots of rooms, normally arranged into corridors or blocks, with either en-suite bathroom facilities or shared bathrooms between several rooms. This arrangement lends itself to the mad dash for the shower in the mornings and 'learning to tolerate others' that is oh so character building. The rooms may well be single occupancy but could just as well involve you having to share with another person, a la US college style.

The key difference compared to other types of hall is the fact that food is provided, with breakfast, possibly lunch, and dinner all prepared by professional caterers and ready for you to tuck into without ever having to reach for a pan. This obviously has massive benefits, especially as eating together in a large hall with all of your mates is a great social experience and a great way of getting to meet as many different people as possible. It also means that you, technically, have more time to devote to both academic and extra-curricular pursuits, whether it be getting involved in societies, sports and other such endeavors. Most halls do provide very rudimentary self-catering facilities, usually in a small room on each floor, complete with a microwave, but these are only really intended for preparing the occasional simple snack as opposed to three course meals. As such, if you are a budding Michelin starred chef then catered halls may not be for you.

One thing to note about catered halls is the fact that although the mealtimes do run for a reasonable period of time, thus allowing as many students to attend as possible, there will be times when, as a vet student, you won't be able to make it back or have to leave halls earlier than normal. Although most halls will, with fair warning, try and make allowances for you, the lack of flexibility is something that may become irksome. The quality of the food can also vary considerably between halls, so it is worth trying to chat with students who have been in any catered halls you are considering before you apply in order to get the lowdown on the food. In terms of cost, however, catered halls do prove to be a great deal, assuming you eat there often enough, with many offering heavily subsidised food and ensuring that you get at least one, decent square meal per day, which is not something that is guaranteed in self-catering.

Self-catering halls - as with catered halls, these are often large buildings divided into corridors with shared kitchens, or possibly self-contained flats with several people sharing. I spent my first year in a shared house, which was part of a larger student hall, and we had shared bathrooms and a kitchen, much like living at home except with the need to cook for ourselves and a greater number of indoor water-fights and corridor cricket games! The main advantage of cooking for yourself is that you retain control over what you eat, when you eat and how much you spend. This option does require discipline, especially to avoid falling into the classic student rut of eating nothing but toast, pasta and beans, and I certainly know friends who spent their entire first year surviving on pizza, even using the box as a plate to avoid having to wash up! Half the problem is that scores of students simply do not know how to cook for themselves and don't realise how easy it is to prepare something fresh and healthy and to do so both quickly and cheaply. The benefits of getting into the habit of eating healthily and correctly from the start are clear, with major knock-on advantages for both your academic studies and your general wellbeing. My advice, if you don't know the basics of cooking and preparing food, is to get yourself a simple cookery book and start making the odd meal at home before you're left to fend completely for yourself. Self-catering can also be a fun, sociable option, with cooking and mealtimes a great chance to chat with your flatmates and catch-up on the day's events. There is also the option of hosting dinner for your friends and, of course, impressing that new girlfriend or boyfriend with your culinary skills – much more suave than dragging them along to the cafeteria! In my house each person cooked for themselves every day, which could get a little dull and feel a bit like a chore occasionally, whereas in our second year we developed a house cooking rota, whereby one person would cook for the house each day. The advantages of this were that we had variety in our diets, could spend the time we would normally cook doing other things, and catch up with our flatmates when we all ate together. The other benefit is that it is generally easier and more cost effective to buy, prepare and cook ingredients for a bigger meal than it is to cook for one person, unless you're happy to then eat the same thing for several days.

Colleges – if you take up a place at Cambridge you will more than likely live in your college for at least the first year. As far as I am aware they are all catered, with the option of attending college formals being a great feature, and thus have all the pros and cons of other catered halls.

Private sector – the options above are provided by the university itself and so many of the services which students might take for granted, such as cleaning, are included as part of the fee paid. Some students find themselves in private sector accommodation, either through choice or because they were unable, for whatever reason, to secure university accommodation. As well as, typically, being more expensive than university housing, there are many other things to consider if looking at the private sector, especially for your first year at university.

The cost of renting in the private sector will, likely, be greater than that of university housing and you will probably have to sign a twelve month contract, although some landlords and agencies do offer options for shorter agreements. This is important to check as the difference between paying nine month's worth of rent and then moving out at the end of the academic year, and paying a full year, including the summer when you will probably be back at home, is considerable. There are also 'extra' costs which you may not have thought about and which you wouldn't need to really worry about in halls, such as agency fees, deposits, including deposit-security fees, the costs of cleaning at the end of the tenancy and all the myriad utility bills that you will have to manage yourselves. Some private sector landlords and agencies include the cost of household bills in the monthly rental so you don't have to manage these yourself, but the rent charged tends to be higher as a result.

One potential drawback of living outside of halls and other university accommodation is the risk of feeling socially isolated. Sure, you might hit it off straight away with your new flatmates and become 'best friends forever,' but many people don't immediately click with those that they are forced to live with and the risk of those students becoming withdrawn and choosing to retire to their rooms each day is a serious one, especially if it is the first time they have lived away from the security and comforts of home. These students are the ones most at risk of dropping out of university, something which they will more than likely go on to regret. If you find yourself in the position of having to turn to private sector accommodation in your first year of university please make sure that you develop social connections outside of your house, whether that be with course-mates or by joining a sports team or society. The Fresher Fair, which most universities hold in one form or another during the first few weeks of the new term, is often a great place to start.

At some point during your second or possibly third term in the first year, your thoughts will turn to where and with whom you are going to live in second year. This is, understandably, quite a big deal and can result in a fair amount of stress, drama and general upheaval. The subject of who is going to live with who can, and often does, lead to personal relationships being strained for a variety of reasons, normally as a result of there being differences in opinion over who is going to make up 'the house.' I was lucky in that I had formed a pretty strong and well balanced friendship group, meaning that the six (a good number as well) of us were happy to consider living together. The next task was to choose where to live. You may find that, yet again, opinions as well as budgets differ and coupled with the pressure to find somewhere before they all get snapped up in the crazy melee that is the university 'housing season,' can lead to it being a daunting but also exciting time. One question that always springs to the fore around this time is "to live with vet friends or not to live with vet friends?" This is a personal decision with definite pros and cons to both answers. I, personally, lived with other vets, meaning our dinnertime conversations naturally drifted towards disgusting vet humour such as the fact that our tagliatelli resembled the tapeworms we'd just been studying, whereas many others I know chose to live with hall friends or other non-vet people, delaying living with fellow vets until the clinical years.

Living at Home

Some of you may opt to apply to vet school locally, with the intent being to live at home during your studies. Although this is certainly an option and would be expected to lessen the expense of studying at vet school, it does have its pros and cons, as with most things. The first point to make is that you are not guaranteed to receive an offer from your 'local' vet school, in which case you may have no choice but to move away and live as a typical student. Secondly, much of the fun and experience associated with being at university and especially being a vet student, comes from being away from the home environment and taking a leap into the unknown, both domestically and socially. Although I know vet students who have quite successfully engaged in vet school life whilst living at home I would argue that for most it would represent a challenging juggling act and the risk is that you could end up feeling somewhat sidelined from many of your friends and coursemates. The benefits are, however, clear to see and powerful incentives to remain in the nest. Who can argue with the promise of home-cooked meals or the knowledge that no matter what happens you are guaranteed to be able to return to a nice, warm, comfortable family home? For some the idea of 'escaping' from home is the fantasy that drives their dreams of going to university whereas others love it at home and the ability to study at vet school whilst remaining where they're most happy makes sense. It is a personal decision but one worth pondering carefully.

2. **Finances & Student Loans** - how are you going to live?

University is expensive. There is simply no denying this fact, and with the tuition fees what they now are, your vet school education is going to end up costing significantly more than mine did, which was still a ton of money that I will be paying back for the best part of my life. As such, it is vitally important to have a good grasp on your finances before you head off to start university, and to be able to budget, plan and spend wisely. This will be covered in more detail in the chapter on finance, so you are welcome to flick forward several pages if you want to learn more about all things money.

3. **Course Information** - what happens when you first arrive?

Once you have accepted your place and confirmed it following the publication of exam results, the university and vet school will send you information about what to expect during your first few weeks. This will include timetables and advice for orientation. Some schools also send out notes on reading that they would like you to do before starting the course. I was sent some notes on veterinary anatomy, including anatomical terminology, although must admit that I didn't study it as well as I could or should have! Most will also send things like recommended book and equipment lists, although my advice is do not be tempted to rush out and spend a fortune on new books and the latest designer waterproofs. There is plenty of opportunity to get what you actually, realistically need once you've started and can be sure that what you're buying is essential. Plus, most things like essential textbooks can usually be snapped up second hand from older vet students for a fraction of the 'new' price.

You may also receive information from the vet school's student society, introducing themselves and inviting you to join, as well as offering their own, unique insight into the crazy new world that you are about to dive head first into! At Bristol we sent out our 'Fresher Guide,' which gave new students information on everything from vet socials, including the need, at all times, to be better than the medics at all things, sports teams, specialist interest societies (eg. the zoological society), the role of the veterinary society, and helpful advice on what to expect from subjects, including which books to buy and which to simply borrow from the library. Most also now have excellent websites for students to refer to, including message-boards and forums, and also Facebook groups, which you can use to start chatting with your new course-mates, including current students. All in all, it is incredibly exciting getting such information through the post as it really starts to drive home the reality that you are about to actually fulfil your dream of starting at vet school, which is an awesome feeling!

First Year - What is it actually like?

Your first year will fly by! In fact, the whole of your time at vet school will whizz past so enjoy every moment, even the rubbish, stressful parts. One of the key benefits of being a vet student is that you instantly have a really fantastic social and pastoral care network in place, which most other subjects don't have. In fact, by the time you leave vet school it is highly likely that you will have friends not only in your own year and years above and below you, but also at other schools. Veterinary, as a profession, is relatively small and so can feel like a large extended family. I intercalated in biochemistry during my time at Bristol and was amazed, and a little saddened, by the fact that there were people in the year who had never even spoken to one another for the entire three years of their degree course – the idea of not knowing everyone in my year at vet school just seemed alien and wrong. The one word I would use to describe your first year at university, and specifically vet school, then is 'sociable.'

The first week or two will mainly centre around meeting people, both at the vet school and in halls, getting your head around your timetables and where classes are to be held, and then also just generally settling into life as a free, young, independent new student. This can seem incredibly daunting and it is easy to feel overwhelmed. Please remember, however, that you are not on your own and if you're feeling a bit freaked out by everything then you can be sure that everyone else will be too. These first few weeks can also feel a bit tumultuous socially as you make new friends and form new relationships, probably to then change them within a few weeks until you finally find that group of really good friends that will then be with you through the trials, tribulations and fun of university life and beyond.

Socials

During the first few weeks of the new term most halls and vet student societies put on socials, either during the day as an informal 'meet and greet' or evening events, such as a 'Fresher Party,' where the emphasis will probably be more on having a few cheeky drinks and meeting both the rest of your year, and also the years above you, who will be very interested to see what new talent has been allowed in. Social occasions are not limited to the first few weeks and there are normally lots of hall socials, bar crawls, formal balls, not so formal parties and plenty of opportunities to just go out on the town with your new friends.

The veterinary community is a very sociable one and is one thing that a lot of your non-vet friends will probably be a little envious of – one positive result of spending so much time together, both as part of the course and also socially, is that you really do get to know your year extremely well and, although, you might not become best friends with everyone the fact is that the entire year generally looks out for one another. One fantastic social event to look forward to is the final year holiday, which the vast majority of the year goes on after finishing final vivas at the end of the course. My year went to Turkey for two weeks and the experience of holidaying with 90 other new vets was an incredible one! (Note: one of the advantages of intercalating is that you effectively become part of two years - your former year and the one you re-enter - meaning the potential for two final year holidays. I took this opportunity by the horns and went to Ibiza with my original year, somewhere I had never imagined venturing before, and then Turkey with my graduating year.)

Although first year is important, as is any year, and it is highly advised that you devote a good amount of energy and time to academic work, there is the recognition 'that it is also an important transition year and one during which socialising and adjusting to life as a university student is important. Vet students are renowned for "working hard and playing harder," and this is definitely something that is encouraged from day one!

Societies

As mentioned, each vet school is likely to have their own student society, which fulfils many functions aside from organising great parties each term. They normally represent your views on various academic committees and challenge any potentially contentious changes or additions to the course, as well as organising educational talks and great deals on everything from books to stethoscopes, so it is definitely worth holding off buying anything until you get to university and have seen what the society can do for you.

There is ample opportunity to get actively stuck in and contribute to the running of the society from day one of starting vet school, and it's a really good way of getting to know people in the years above. I started out as a Fresh Rep (organised fresher events and membership packs) at the end of my first year, before becoming editor of our society magazine, Vet News, with my friend and flatmate, Nathan, before securing the top job of Centaur President. I loved my time working for the society and really enjoyed the feeling of camaraderie that went with working closely with a group of like-minded, committed and skilled people to achieve common goals and enrich the lives of our fellow vet students.

AVS (Association of Vet Students)

This is the student division of the BVA (British Veterinary Association) and represents UK and Irish vet students at a national level. They publish a magazine (JAVS), conduct regular surveys of matters such as student debt, and organise an annual congress, at which new committee members are elected from the student membership. They also organise the mother of all socials in the form of the AVS Sports Weekend. Despite the word 'sport' in the title, this weekend has become less about the athletic endeavours of the various vet schools and more focused on the dedicated socialisation that occurs. Each year one of the vet schools host students from all of the other schools with each university having their own fancy dress themes (the final year usually have their own theme), thus enabling you to see at a glance where everyone has come from. I have particularly fond memories of spending weekends dressed as a Buddhist monk, Brownie, Mime Artist, Gladiator and Captain Jack Sparrow – the best weekend of my life so far! To say that AVS is fun would be an understatement and it is well worth making sure you get to go on at least one whilst you are at vet school. More information about AVS can be found on their website at www.avs-uk.org.uk.

IVSA (International Veterinary Students' Association)

This society does many things including organising student exchange programmes between various countries. They also hold annual congresses and symposia, which are fantastic opportunities to travel to different parts of the world, meet vet students from different cultures and exchange ideas and experiences. They are also actively involved in supporting veterinary education around the globe, especially in disadvantaged countries, and represent the professional interests of vet students the world over. If you have an international outlook and would like to know more about the IVSA then you can visit their website at www.ivsa.org.

There are many other societies that you will be able to join as a vet student, including the various species specific organisations, such as the BSAVA (British Small Animal Veterinary Association) and BEVA (British Equine Veterinary Association), and most offer free membership to students, as well as offering you the chance to steward at their respective annual congresses.

Its not all veterinary though, and there are as many student societies as there are ideas in the world, with pretty much every interest catered for. If you can't find a student society that covers your particular hobby or interest then you could always get funding from the university to establish one yourself!

Sports

Are you a budding sports star? Even if you're not, there are so many opportunities to play and get involved in sport at university, that you might just find it hard not to become active. If you are a serious sportsperson then the university teams should be your first port of call. Many vet students successfully juggle their studies, a social life and training and playing at a high level for their university. Even if you're not university team standard, or just don't fancy the commitment of playing at a high level, then there are plenty of opportunities to get involved in sport through student halls and the societies themselves. When I was at Bristol we had really good hockey, football and rugby teams, with the latter even going on tour to Barbados one year!

Creativity

Not only are vets a talented bunch academically and at sport, but they also tend to be pretty creative too. There are a plethora of creative activities for you to get involved in during your time at vet school, from contributing to annual pantomimes, which normally focus on some heavy-duty piss-taking of clinical and teaching staff, to writing articles for the society magazine or even JAVS (the AVS magazine) and even playing in a band. So whether you're a skilled costume designer, budding writer or comedian, or even a wannabe rock star you'll find plenty of opportunities to flex your creative muscles. Then, of course, there are the huge number of fancy dress events that you'll get to go to. Vets do love dressing up and its not uncommon for us to leave university with a bigger comedy wardrobe than we have normal clothes!

Initiations

Despite the rumours that will inevitably circulate when you get to vet school, the initiations, which were once commonplace and could be a bit of an ordeal, are significantly tamer affairs than they ever used to be, and in fact I don't think they're even really allowed to use the term 'initiation.' Gone are the days of running round the countryside, wading through slurry whilst being made to down 'special' cider. They are still entertaining, fun events and definitely a right of passage, with many of those who don't take part later saying that they regret it. They are also a fantastically funny way of getting to know your new year better and provide hours of pub-banter material!

EMS (Extra-Mural Studies)

This has already been touched upon in an earlier chapter but it is worth just considering what to expect from placements during your first year. For most vet students, their first experience of EMS will be over the Easter holidays, when they will be sent to a farm somewhere in the country in order to help with lambing. Different students' experiences will vary greatly, with some boasting about cushy hours, great food and payment – this is not normal, and EMS is a voluntary, unpaid aspect of the course - for their efforts, whilst others may have had to contend with doing nightshifts and living in less-than-desirable accommodation. Either way, everyone comes back to university in the summer with great stories and a real sense of why they are studying to become a vet.

The next 'dose' of EMS usually comes during the summer vacation between first and second year, and it is usually necessary to devote at least half the time to completing various pre-clinical placements. This, obviously, eats into your 'free time' and does limit your ability to earn much-needed cash during the holidays, something we will discuss in more detail in the chapter on finance, but is a requirement of the degree and, on the whole, a richly rewarding experience.

Exams & Assessments

Unfortunately these do feature as part of being a vet student and you will need to get used to doing them a lot, and in various different forms. From traditional written papers to multiple-choice exams, steeplechases (a series of exhibits are set up and the year moves around each, with a set amount of time to answer a question on each of them), computer-based assessments, and vivas (spoken exams), the range of exams is vast. Then, of course, there are projects, both group and individual, and assessment whilst on rotation in your final year.

Although the exams can be daunting, the key thing to remember is that you do already know how to prepare for and perform well in exams, otherwise you wouldn't really be able to consider veterinary as a career option. The key difference with veterinary exams is that there isn't really a set syllabus that you can work through and be sure of getting 100% if you cover everything. Instead, the material covered in your lectures and practical sessions tends to represent the basic level of knowledge required for a pass, with any desire to achieve higher than a pass – which for veterinary is typically 50% - requiring further reading around subjects, both from textbooks and, ideally, journals, which are the best source for the most current thinking on any subject. Getting access to textbooks and journals will be easy as all of the vet schools and universities have excellent libraries and most will permit electronic access to journals if you have a university logon.

Most of the vet schools will have exams either before or after the Christmas break in first year, and then, again, in the summer. The exact exam schedule and breakdown for the year will vary between vet schools and may even alter from year to year so it is best to check these details with the vet schools that you are specifically interested in applying to. Needless to say, vet students are assessed a lot and so if the thought of at least another five or six years of exams terrifies you then you might not like veterinary too much.

One other potential culture shock associated with becoming a vet student is the fact that you may suddenly find that you are no longer the smartest kid in your year. Vet students are, on the whole, a bright bunch and will have been near, if not at, the top of their year, academically-speaking, when at school. Collecting all these bright sparks together suddenly highlights the fact that some students are even more hard-working or just plain gifted than even you, and this can come as a bit of a surprise. You may find that you go from routinely scoring marks of 90% plus in exams when at school to being ecstatic to achieve a pass mark of 50% and make it through to the next year. For vet students the new Holy Grail of academic achievement becomes a mark of about 75%, which at most schools represents the distinction borderline. This, however, is a target that, despite their best efforts, many vet students don't reach. I was always advised that as long as you manage to work hard enough to stay in the middle third of your year in terms of academic achievement (so, an exam mark of about 60-65%) then you should be okay and still be able to devote time and energy to extra-curricular activities. How hard you work, and the standard you set for yourself is, of course, a matter for personal choice and if you have your sights firmly set on graduating with honours then go for it.

Vivas

These deserve a special mention as the only experience most of you may have had of these will be the oral exam as part of your language courses at school, such as French. Vivas are, basically, verbal exams and each one usually lasts no more than about fifteen to twenty minutes. You may find yourself being "viva'd" for different reasons. When I was in first year, every student had an anatomy viva, during which you would go to different anatomical specimens and be asked questions about it by the examiner. Most other subjects reserve the use of vivas for those students who are on borderlines, either between pass/ fail, pass/merit or merit/ distinction, and the wait for the 'viva list' each summer is an anxious one for most. In final year, all students have vivas as part of their final veterinary assessments and passing these leads to you being awarded your veterinary degree. As such, any practice you can get of explaining things to someone else verbally, even during revision, is great preparation for vivas.

SUMMARY

Life at vet school is great fun and finally finding yourself at uni as a real-life vet student is a brilliant realisation of the dream! Your time will fly past in a flash and although it is a tough course to get through, the fun that is had makes all of the exams, revision and academic headaches worth it. It is a great idea, if you can, to try and talk to as many current students, both veterinary and other subjects, before you actually apply to vet school in order to gain some deeper understanding of what you can expect from your time at university. If you want to learn more about my own, personal experiences then you can always check out my personal account, The Nerdy Vet's Vet School Success, which I have been told is a pretty funny and insightful read. The take home message, however, is to prepare for your big move in good time and then just enjoy being a vet student - it truly is one of the best times of your life!

Gavin Turley
BVM&S MRCVS
Online Marketing Manager at
zooplus.co.uk

I graduated from Edinburgh in 2006 and 6 years on I'm now working in the heart of historic Oxford as the Online Marketing Manager for zooplus.co.uk – Europe's largest online pet supplies company. Instead of the usual activities of a vet, a large part of my day is spent managing the marketing budget on Google to ensure I reach my new customer targets! With no on-call my day finishes at 5pm which allows me plenty of time to relax outside of working hours and keep myself fit.

Different Career Path after Vet School

1. When did you first decide that you wanted to be a vet?

I only really decided to become a vet because I wasn't too sure what else to do! My older brother had already qualified as a vet from Cambridge before the time came for me to apply to universities and given that I had the grades for veterinary I thought it seemed like a good thing to do!

2. When did you decide that you didn't want to work as a vet? What prompted your career change?

I really struggled through the early part of vet school – it's a tough course and if your heart isn't in it then it's difficult to find the motivation to put all the hours of study in. Yet my problem was that I didn't know what else I wanted to do and everyone told me that as soon as I got to the clinical years things would be much better! Unfortunately that wasn't the case but thankfully the social side of vet school and playing rugby kept me going, plus the fear of failing! By the time I got to final year I knew veterinary wasn't for me. All I had to do was 2 things – 1. Pass and 2. Figure out what I was going to do!

3. What was the reaction of friends and family to your decision not to work as a vet? How did you respond?

The friends closest to me, the majority of whom were vet students themselves, had seen me struggle for a few years so it wasn't a surprise to them that I didn't want to be a vet but even still, their question and mine was what would I do if I wasn't going to be a vet?! For my family it came as a bit more of a shock as I hadn't always been as open about my situation with them! I think my mum still thinks that one day I will return to veterinary!!

4. What have you done since graduating from vet school?

After graduating the first job I got was with an online veterinary pharmacy – they needed a vet or pharmacist to dispense the prescription drugs. This was perfect for me as it was using my degree but didn't involve seeing any animals!

As the business was relatively small I was also handed the task of managing the Google AdWords account in between dispensing orders. I had no idea what AdWords was but quickly learnt it was Google's only source of income and how companies paid Google to have their results shown on the first page of search results. I read books about AdWords, went to conferences, listened to webinars – I loved the challenge of AdWords and the complexity of managing a budget with the aim of getting a profitable return on investment.

After 1 year I left my position at the online pharmacy and became self-employed. I went out and found businesses I could help to manage their AdWords accounts. After a year I joined a marketing agency working with larger clients, then I went travelling for 2 years during which I continued freelance AdWords work – all I need is an internet connection! Upon my return to the UK I joined zooplus.co.uk and that's where I am now!

5. How, if at all, did your veterinary training/ time at vet school prepare you for a career outside of clinical veterinary?

The training I received at vet school was invaluable in many ways – learning how to speak to a client, how to ask the right questions and listen to the answers is a skill which can be transferred to any discipline in life. Communication and the confidence to believe in your own abilities is essential in any job you do and vet school gave me a lot of those skills.

6. What does your current role entail?

Basically I spend a lot of money every day! All I have to do is ensure the money I spend generates new customers for the business at a sustainable cost. I spend a lot of my time working with Google and have my own Google account manager. I've been to the Google European headquarters in Dublin as well as their office in Munich for various meetings. As zooplus is Europe wide I have colleagues doing a similar job to me in Germany, France, Spain, Italy, Poland, Holland, Denmark and Sweden so I'm always in contact with them as we try new things and develop our marketing strategy.

7. What do you most enjoy about your current job?

When I was younger I always said that I would never work in an office – I didn't want to be stuck inside looking at a computer screen all day – look at me now! But in reality I find it much better than going out on calls in the rain or dealing with anal glands! Plus I find my job interesting – it's a daily challenge to manage the marketing spend – I need to keep on top of so many variables – what promotions our competitors are running, do we have enough stock, are our prices at the right level! Every day brings something new.

8. Do you keep in touch with former coursemates/ vets?

I'm still very much in touch with the veterinary world as my wife is a small animal vet. Plus the friends I made at vet school are lifelong so vet chat is never far away – as the years go by my knowledge is definitely diminishing (not that it was ever any good in the first place) as now I'm happy if I remember even the most basic veterinary fact.

9. Do you ever miss clinical veterinary?

In a word – no! Veterinary was never for me and I would have been miserable if I had forced myself to continue in the profession.

10. Where do you see yourself in five years? Ten years?

Unless my lottery numbers come up, in which case I'll be travelling the world following sporting events, I would imagine I'll still be in the same industry. My role may have diversified by then as I gather more knowledge and experience but I'd be surprised if I wasn't working for an online business helping them to generate lots of profit!

11. Some people would say that not working as a vet after graduating means that you wasted your training. What would your response be to that statement?

In some respects I agree – it costs a lot of money to train a vet. However a vet can have a working life of 40+ years and if it isn't right for them then it's best to get out as soon as possible! I was 17 when I decided to apply to vet school and even then I wasn't 100% sure I wanted to do it. Just because veterinary is classed as a vocational degree doesn't mean a graduate should be tied to it for the rest of their life!

12. What advice would you offer to someone currently at vet school who might be having doubts about their career options?

At the end of the day veterinary is just a degree. Look at how many students get a degree in history, arts, geography and maths and go on to do something completely different to what they studied. You have to do what makes you happy and although turning your back on veterinary is a very difficult thing to do it is possible.

13. What general advice would you offer someone considering applying to vet school?

Make sure it is for you as the reality of being a vet is a lot different to what you see on TV. Compared to other professions such as medicine, veterinary is underpaid yet just as difficult to qualify in. See practice, speaks to vets, understand it's not just cute puppies and adorable calves — there is much more to it than that. Then if you are still convinced it's for you go for it!

14. Any additional information that you would like to include.

Never feel obligated to work as a vet even if you qualify as one — if you've got that far you've proved your capabilities and there will be plenty of employers who would relish having your skills in their business.

VET SCHOOL

3 : FINANCES

Training to become a vet is expensive. There is simply no getting away from this fact. With the cost of going to university ever-increasing and with tuition fees, especially for highly sought-after courses such as veterinary, at the levels that they are, average debt values amongst UK veterinary graduates have been on the rise, with the current average debt on graduation being in the region of £45,000, although finding accurate figures is difficult so it may even be more than this and is, I am certain, set to rise considerably in the coming years. Factor in living expenses, which many students cover through student loans, and it is not difficult to see veterinary graduates leaving university with debts in excess of £80,000! Why does it cost so much to go to university, and especially to train as a vet? What sources of funding are available and how can you afford to go to vet school? Read on for the answers. Please note that the majority of the commentary in this chapter is targeted at UK home students, and especially those studying in England, although there is consideration for those students from Scotland, Wales, Northern Ireland, the EU and International students, so fear not.

Why does it cost so much to go to Vet School?

There are a number of factors that contribute to the overall high cost of studying for a veterinary degree, and these are:

Vet School: Part Two

Tuition fees

The average annual tuition fee for UK veterinary courses is now £9000, with international students having to pay closer to £20,000 per year. So, for a home student studying veterinary science as their first degree the cost of tuition alone over five years is £45,000! This is a marked change to what it was even when I was studying, and the cost of graduating as a vet is huge compared to many currently qualified vets' experiences. The argument for this high level of tuition is that universities need to charge higher fees to fund continued investment in research and teaching to enable them to compete in a global higher education market and attract the best minds to work and teach at them, thus raising the standard of education overall. It is difficult to argue with this but the danger is that it may soon become prohibitively expensive for those from more modest backgrounds, and whose families can't afford to provide significant financial support, to consider vet school and will not be able to consider training as vets. A narrowing in the demographic of the profession would not be a positive move and would go completely against the aim of the profession to increase diversity and access. Contrary to popular belief, vets do not earn huge salaries and so the incentive or return on initial investment may simply no longer be present for a lot of students, who would otherwise have made fantastic vets. There may also be a drive for good veterinary undergraduates to gain their degrees outside of the UK, with many schools now offering veterinary courses, often taught in English and at a fraction of the cost of completing the course here at home.

EMS Costs

Completing EMS (Extra-Mural Studies) placements is a requirement of the Royal College of Veterinary Surgeons and so a significant proportion of vet students' vacation time is spent seeing practice with a variety of different providers. Although vet students and the profession as a whole places great value on the merits of the EMS scheme, there is ongoing debate about the costs associated with it. It is estimated, by some sources, that the total cost of EMS over the entire duration of the course could be as high as 5-10% of the total average student debt, so between £2,000 and 4,500. But why?

1. ***Cost of attending EMS*** – Not everyone is able to access the placements they need or want from home and so many students either have to commute long distances each day or find and pay for accommodation in order to be able to attend placements. I know friends who were routinely having to drive 80 mile round trips each day to get to their foster practice, and others who had to pay for B&B or hotel rooms for the duration of their placements, which can be anything up to three weeks in length. It doesn't take a degree in maths to work out that the costs can soon rocket! There is no payment made to the student for any of these placements,

although some types, such as lambing, do sometimes offer students a small amount for their efforts. As such, veterinary students routinely find themselves considerably out of pocket in their bid to complete their EMS.

2. **Inability to work during holidays** – Due to the fact that vet students have to complete EMS during vacations, they are thus unable to seek paid employment during university holidays. This lack of earning power further compounds the debt incurred during the holidays and means that vet students routinely start the new university year in a worse financial state than their non-veterinary peers.

No Government Support

Medical and dental students can expect to receive government support in the form of NHS bursaries, which help towards funding a large part of their training. Although they are expected to 'repay' some of this support by working in the NHS after graduation, the truth is that doctors and dentists can expect to earn considerably more than their veterinary counterparts, perhaps not immediately but certainly within a few years.

It is true that veterinary medicine is, for the most part, private medicine and so there is no obligation on the government to fund the education and training of it's future practitioners and beneficiaries. However, how many of you have private medical or dental cover and pay handsomely for their services? Is it fair that these medics and dentists enjoy financial support during their training to then go out and work in private practice? This is an area ripe for debate. It could easily be argued that vets do contribute to the health of the nation by, for example, monitoring and enforcing rules which protect us from a range of potentially zoonotic diseases and helping to ensure the smooth running of the nation's farms and, thus, the food supply. What about the millions of family pets which are cared for by the nation's small animal vets and thus help maintain the mental wellbeing of their owners, probably saving the NHS millions of pounds per year? Perhaps there is a case, after all, for more government support to be directed towards veterinary students, although I very much doubt that will happen anytime soon. One thing that should be taken into account is the fact that, as mentioned, vet students are not as able to work during holidays as their peers and so maybe making allowances for this through, for example, a reduction in the tuition fees charged would be a good measure. You may have some good ideas yourself.

Living Costs

If you've ever lived away from home then you'll be aware of just how expensive life can be, from paying for food to rent, utility bills, clothes, books and actually having a bit of a life as well. Its staggering really how easily the 'cost of living' can rise, with an average figure for students of about £7,000 per year being cited.

This will obviously vary depending on a whole range of factors, from your own particular lifestyle (Primark versus Prada, for example), to the course you study and equipment required, right the way through to where in the country you are studying and, therefore, what rents and bills are like. Most of the university websites now offer links to pages giving an idea of the likely living costs associated with attending their school and they are worth taking a look at.

Sources of Funding

There are, in essence, two types of funding available: that which you and your family are able to provide; and funding from external sources, notably the government, although other organisations may be able to help.

Government Support

Although the heady days of generous grants and carefree student living are long-gone, there are a number of options available for those wanting to access state support, including grants if you are eligible. For state support and sources of funding you will need to apply directly to Student Finance (www.direct.gov.uk, and follow links to Student Finance), allowing plenty of time to submit the relevant information required and for this to be processed. It is highly recommended that you apply for funding long before you accept a place at university, with applications really needing to be in by April of the year you plan to attend university.

1. **Tuition Fee Loan** – This is not assessed depending on household income (what your parents earn) and is intended to cover the full cost of tuition each year, and can be up to £9000 each year. This money is paid directly to your university, so as long as you have submitted your application in time and correctly then you don't really need to worry about this. As it says in the title, this is a loan and, as such, has to be repaid, although there are certain conditions that have to be met before this happens (see below).

2. **Maintenance Grant and the Special Support Grant** – Both of these are intended to help students with the cost of accommodation and other living costs whilst on full-time higher education courses, and do not have to repaid like loans. The maximum available is about £3,300 for each, and students are only eligible for one or the other. Maintenance Grants are income-assessed and the amount you get also depends on other factors, such as when you started your course. The amount you are awarded in Maintenance Grant may also lead to a reduction in the amount of Maintenance Loan you are eligible to apply for. Special Support Grants, which are not income assessed and do not affect the amount of loan available to you, are only available to students who are deemed a 'prescribed person' under the Income Support or Housing Benefit Regulations, and include single parents and students with certain

disabilities. You are advised to consult the Student Finance website for more information and to check whether you are eligible for either of these grants. Both are paid directly into your bank account at the start of each term.

3. **_Maintenance Loan_** – This is intended to help cover the cost of accommodation and other living costs, with the maximum available just over £4,300 if living at home or £5,500 if living away from home, although more is available if you're studying in London. The amount you are eligible to apply for is calculated based on a number of factors, including your household income, whether you plan to live at home during your studies or away, when you started your course, whether you're in your final year, and also how much, if any, Maintenance Grant you are eligible to receive. All students are eligible to receive a proportion of the maximum amount, with the rest being dependent on the factors discussed.

Reapplying for Support

One important thing to remember about accessing state support is that you have to reapply for it each year. This is something that its really easy to overlook and forget about whilst you're in the midst of studying and/ or partying hard so it's worth pencilling it into your diaries a good year in advance. If there is one time that you will definitely need that student loan and grant then its certainly once you've actually started university!

Repaying Loans

As mentioned, loans, unless you're very lucky and the lender forgets about you, need to be repaid and student loans are no exception. The good news, however, is that you don't have to start repaying them immediately after graduation, with repayment commencing from the April after you have graduated, and only if you are earning over £21,000 per year. This means that if you end up deciding to jet off and travel for a year, or volunteer your veterinary services to charity, and earn under the threshold then you wont automatically start paying it back. Once you do start repaying it, you will automatically have 9% of whatever you earn kindly taken out of your pay each month, although if you wish to repay the loan faster then you can opt to pay more each time. One thing to note is that if you do any additional work, or earn money in a self-employed capacity, then you'll need to declare this and be prepared to put aside 9% of what you earn for student loan repayments, in addition to any tax payable on the amount. Student loans do, contrary to popular belief, accrue interest on the balance and this starts building up from the date the money is first paid out until it is paid off. Having said this, the interest is normally very small and student loans are still, at present, one of the most cost-effective ways of borrowing money available. Whether this will always remain the case is unclear.

Students from places other than England can find out more about accessing state funding by visiting the following websites:

Northern Ireland	**www.studentfinanceni.co.uk**
Scotland	**www.saas.gov.uk**
Wales	**www.studentfinancewales.co.uk**
European Union (EU)	EU students can access student loans if studying in England, Wales and Northern Ireland. Visit **www.direct.gov.uk**
International Students	**www.ukcisa.org.uk**

University Assistance

1. **Bursaries & Scholarships** – These are extra sources of financial assistance on top of grants and loans, and may be paid out in cash or in other forms, such as discounts on accommodation or free books and travel. They don't have to be repaid and can be accessed either by directly contacting your university or, in some cases, by Student Finance, or the equivalent, sharing your financial information with your university. This will, of course, only ever be done with your permission. If in doubt it is always best to check with your vet school to see what process they prefer. Intercalation normally attracts very generous bursaries and scholarships, with The

Wellcomme Trust proving to be big supporters of students who wish to take advantage of the scheme.

2. **Charitable Trusts** – There are a number of charities and trusts who provide financial assistance to students in higher education, and you may be able to get an award from one of these organisations on top of what you already receive in the form of loans and grants. You can get advice on accessing grants from the Educational Grants Advisory Service (EGAS), and from both your university and most public libraries.

The key with accessing external sources of funding is to ask. If you're not sure what help is available then make a point of contacting the vet school, the university finance office and the other sources mentioned so far. Again, as with most things in life, if you don't ask then you won't get.

Other Sources of Funding

It is unlikely that you will be able to cover all of the costs associated with attending university full-time through the sources given so far, and you will therefore need to consider some or all of the following to help make up the short-fall:

1. **Savings** – some students are lucky enough, or perhaps just have enough foresight, to have accumulated savings before

going to university. If you are able to put aside some money, even if a small amount, before starting vet school then it will certainly make a difference and will help to delay that gut-wrenching moment when you realise that you have officially entered into your overdraft! Some of you may have decided to take a Gap Year in order to work and earn money for university and this is certainly a good option, although in my experience, things rarely pan out this way and the temptation to use the money to head off and travel is normally too strong to resist. You may, of course, be stronger than me though!

2. ***Parental/ Family Contributions*** – Your family will 'contribute' whether directly or not as the amount you receive in Maintenance Grant and Loan is dependent on household income. Your parents and family may be able to help you directly with costs, and this can prove to be extremely helpful. Some parents gift this money to their kids (a kind of grant, if you like) whilst others may make the money available as a "loan," although the terms from 'Bank of Mum and Dad' are normally far better than any you'd get from the regular bank, such as interest free and nice long repayment periods! I was able to support myself financially through the first four years of university, through a combination of student loans, overdrafts and paid employment, with my parents then very kindly assisting me by paying my rent during the last two years when it was impossible to work during the course or holidays. Without

this help I would have been in even more debt than I currently am.

3. **Bank Overdrafts** – These provide a much needed lifeline to most students at some point during their time at university, and the point at which you first enter your overdraft is a memorable and gut-wrenching one. I remember mine vividly as it was one of those "oh shit" moments! Most banks and building societies offer interest-free overdrafts, often with the option of extending the limit, normally as part of a 'Student Account.' It is easy to get seduced by all the weird and wonderful enticements on offer when looking around for a student account, with typical offers for signing up including travel cards and MP3 players, but my advice would be to try and look past the gimmicky 'gifts' and look at the actual terms of the account instead. What you really want from a student account is one which has a generous interest-free overdraft facility and which extends for the duration of your time at university, including a period of time after graduation before they start charging interest. Another key factor to consider is whether you will be able to access banking services easily when you are at university. It is all very well using internet banking to check your account balance and transfer money from the comfort of your room, but occasionally you will want to actually go down to a branch and speak to a human. Such times normally coincide with some sort of acute financial crisis and it is much less stressful being able to discuss your needs face-

to-face with a friendly, local bank manager than to either have to travel miles or do everything over the phone.

4. **Paid Employment** – Some vet students find the time to engage in part-time employment during term-time, such as bar work, although it is difficult as the vet course is both academically challenging and time-consuming. Plus, it seems a crying shame that whilst some students are able to take advantage of the myriad opportunities to engage in new and exciting extra-curricular activities, thus expanding their social network and skill base, many feel they have to use the time to work instead in order to remain solvent. Although it is possible to work for some of the holidays, although only during the earlier years, EMS requirements make it very difficult to earn any meaningful amounts unless you are fortunate enough to be able to secure a job that also satisfies some of the EMS requirements, such as lambing or dairy work. I was fortunate enough to find a milking and calving job on a diary farm for the majority of the summer vacation between both the first and second and then second and third years of my course. Such opportunities are, however, very few and far between. Some universities, notably Cambridge, actually discourage students from working during term-time due to the demands of the course and so it may not be easy to find paid employment anyway. If you do have to work then it is a good idea to look for opportunities to "work smarter, not harder." This means trying to maximise the value of your time, for example by

working for the university, who tend to pay more than the private sector and are more sympathetic to the needs of students, or doing 'skilled' jobs such as tutoring. A few friends and I were employed as personal tutors, through an agency, during our third and fourth years. This was a great job as we were paid much more per hour than any typical student job, meaning that we were either able to earn a lot more than we would normally or reduce the number of hours that we needed to work, thus enabling us to devote the time to academic work or 'fun.'

5. ***Entrepreneurialism*** – Is there something that you can do which could provide a source of income (and is within the limits of the law)? For example, perhaps you are a skilled singer or guitarist and could establish a band to play at weddings and parties for a fee. Maybe you have a skill, such as dancing, which you could teach to others, again, for a fee. One friend of mine earned a good amount of money at university teaching street-dancing to kids at a local school, and only had to work one evening a week! Maybe you have an excellent idea for a business. Most universities actively encourage entrepreneurs and you may find lots of help and resources available to help you turn that idea into cash. Students are a resourceful bunch and it can be amazing the range of money-making schemes that are thought up at university.

6. ***Professional & Career Development Loans (PCDL)*** – These are bank loans that are available to students on a

range of different courses, including the final two years of the vet course. You make an agreement with a participating bank to borrow between £300 and £10,000 and the interest is paid for you whilst you study, and for one month after you finish, with interest then being payable at a rate fixed when you took the loan out. The interest rates charged are set so that they are competitive with other 'unsecured' personal loans available, which is typically 5-6% APR over the lifetime of the loan, which could be anything up to 5 years. For more information on PCDLs, visit www.direct.gov.uk and go to 'Education and Learning.'

7. ***Sponsorship*** - I have noticed a bit of a growing trend in this internet and social media age of students setting up sponsorship pages and asking members of the general public and profession to sponsor them. I think its clearly a symptom of the huge costs associated with studying to be a vet that this is happening and although I applaud such students for seeking out solutions to the very real issues of paying for a veterinary education, I would advise exercising some caution if you plan to go down the same road. For starters, I suspect that more and more students are going to be trying to play the 'sponsor me' card and as with most things, with increased competition comes a reduction in the novelty value of the proposition and a need to make a compelling offer. Why should people sponsor you? What are they going to get in return? Its not enough to simply rely on people looking for that "nice warm, fuzzy feeling" associated with charitable

giving because, to be honest, there are a million and one good causes out there all vying for our wallets' attention. What sets you apart? Be prepared, as well, for the cries of "why on Earth should I pay for you to go to university to qualify as a professional?!" Its a valid point and one which I strongly advise having a good answer for. At the end of the day you're going to wrack up debt but then you're going to get a job at the end of it and earn money. Surely its therefore your decision to 'invest' in yourself and a bit cheeky to ask others, especially those you don't know, to contribute to what is essentially your future earning potential. A better idea? Produce something of value and try and sell it. That is surely a much better idea than relying upon charitable donations.

Managing Your Finances

Once you have funding and money in your pocket it is essential that you know how to look after it, as it is easier to spend money than generate it! Although budgeting, and other such activities, might seem like a really dull activity and something that your parents would be expected to do, they are vital life skills and getting them right during your time at university will help make life a little bit easier.

1. **Budgeting** – The key to budgeting is having awareness and control over two key factors: Income and Expenses. Your

'income' will include sources of cash such as maintenance loans and grants, and any parental or personal money you receive, whereas 'expenses' represent all of the things that cause money to be spent, such as rent, food and other such items. It is worthwhile getting into the habit of budgeting now, before university, so that you have an idea of how it works and how useful and vital an exercise it is. Sit down and write out, either on a piece of paper or on a spreadsheet, the money that you receive each week, month or year, and then the things that cost you money, or are expected to do so for the same time period. Expenses include everything from food, rent, utility bills, insurance premiums (eg. car insurance), money for books, clothes, club memberships, socialising (this is a category which is usually always grossly underestimated when budgeting), and travel. You may even be able to add more to this list, which is by no means, exhaustive. One thing that will probably become clear quite quickly is how much each of us actually spends, and how there usually isn't much difference between what we earn and what we spend. The key with budgeting is to identify opportunities to increase the income amount whilst either reducing, or minimising, the expenses column. You might, for example, see that you routinely spend a lot each week on clubbing and could easily reduce this expense by going out a little less, or drinking less when you are out. The other merit of budgeting is to enable you to prioritise your spending. For example, paying your rent is more important than buying that new dress, although it might not feel like that right now, so making sure you have money available in your account to pay said rent is important. You could also work out how much money you have available each week and try and stick to a 'budget.' This way, if you end the week under-budget then the money you 'save' could be added to the next week's budget or put towards something special, like a holiday. Simple, small measures and changes such as these can, over time, make a big difference to the state of your finances and keep you out of the financial danger zone for longer. It is the students who go crazy at the start of term, when their loans suddenly fill their accounts with cash, and go out on mad spending sprees that soon find themselves in real financial trouble. Don't be one of them.

2. **Discounts** – We all love a bargain and once you get to university you'll soon come to love them even more. Its amazing how reluctant you become to pay full price for anything once you're on a tight budget and so it is a great idea to start keeping your eyes peeled for the plethora of discounts that are available all around us. From book sales, which are normally held a couple of weeks into term, to supermarket offers, such as the classic 'Buy One, Get One Free,' you'll see there are discounts to be had everywhere you normally go. Loads of shops, pubs, clubs, restaurants and leisure providers offer generous student discounts and remember, if you don't ask then you won't get! There are an ever growing number of discount and cashback websites as well, which can, if used smartly, result in some considerable

savings. Another smart, but dangerous if not used with discipline, move is to make use of a cashback credit card for your monthly expenses, meaning that you get money back each time you use it. This does rely on being very self-disciplined and ensuring that you set up a direct debit from your main account to pay the card off automatically each month in full, otherwise debt levels can skyrocket.

3. **Lifestyle Changes** – As already alluded to, small changes in spending habits and lifestyle can make a big difference to the state of your finances. This doesn't mean that you have to change who you are and the things that you really enjoy doing and spending your money on. Rather, its about finding those ways of achieving the same aim whilst spending a little less doing them. For example, could you easily cycle instead of driving? How about taking a little more time to walk into town instead of paying for a bus or taxi? It might take longer but, over a few weeks, you'll save a packet and feel fitter. Why not make lunch occasionally instead of always eating at the expensive neighbourhood café? Maybe you could consider buying certain own-brand groceries and toiletries instead of always reaching for the overpriced premium brands – half of them taste and do the same things anyway but at half the price! If you want any money-saving tips then the best people to ask for advice are current students, so it is worth finding yourself a friendly university student to learn from.

4. **Good Banking Relations** – This goes hand-in-hand with budgeting, as by doing this you will be regularly keeping

an eye on your bank account balance and so will be able to see if you are likely to face a potential funding issue way in advance of the event itself. This will enable you to contact your bank in plenty of time and discuss your requirements with the staff at the branch, who will be able to help where they can. Banks like order and organisation. What they hate is panic, and the last thing they want is for the first contact they have with you to be you crying and begging them for an extension on your overdraft NOW because you're suddenly £500 in the red. They will be a lot more sympathetic and helpful if they can see that you've tried to keep some control over your finances and are responsible with money.

SUMMARY

Training to be a vet is a costly business. Not only is the course a lengthy one but there are a range of additional factors which can lead to debt levels among vet graduates being markedly higher than other students. There are a number of funding sources available to help you pay your way through university, some of which you may not even have to pay back at the end of the course. Which is nice.

Controlling your finances and knowing how to budget effectively is a vital life skill and there is no time like the present to learn how to do it.

Although it is expensive to go to university and you will, unless you're very fortunate, leave vet school with considerable levels of debt, the career prospects for vets are still good meaning that the cost of fulfilling the dream of qualifying as a veterinary surgeon is, for many, still worth the expense.

Alwyn Evans BVetMed

Veterinary Surgeon & Principal
Partner, Moor Cottage
Veterinary Hospital (Berkshire)

Alwyn graduated in 1986 from the Royal Veterinary College, London and is currently Principal Partner at Moor Cottage Veterinary Hospital, where he enjoys running a busy first-opinion practice and providing a first-class service to the hospital's clients. Outside of work, Alwyn enjoys a whole range of activities. Although his triathlon career may be over following hip surgery, he still enjoys keeping active by swimming and cycling, and has recently taken up both yoga and golf. On a less energetic level, Alwyn enjoys traveling anywhere new, especially with his family, reading and music, with his collection being kept bang up to date with the influence of his younger staff and children. An interest in contemporary art, especially Welsh artists, is another of Alwyn's passions. Food is also a particular enjoyment for Alwyn, both dining out and cooking himself, making use of the fare he grows himself. Next on the list is photography....

Vet in Business

1. Had you always seen yourself running your own practice? When did the idea start to appeal?

Yes. The idea really started to take shape about two to three years post qualifying.

2. How did you start your career?

Mixed practice in North Wales where I had seen practice. The owner took a six month sabbatical so I helped his assistant to run the practice in his absence.

3. How did you initially become involved in the more 'businessy' aspects of veterinary?

About two years after qualifying, I decided to do some locum work for about eighteen months, in order to gain experience at practices around the country, and thus learn from different people about how to run a practice. I was employed to run a small animal hospital where I had previously been a locum. The hospital was one of four owned by two vets who did very little clinical work. Six years later I bought the hospital, which is where I am now.

4. **What did you find most challenging when you first started running your own business?**

Time management between clinical and business aspects of practice.

5. **Were there any skills or knowledge that you had to develop early on that were necessary to be able to run your practice? If so, where did you turn to acquire these skills and knowledge?**

Accountancy, payroll, book keeping. I learnt from a couple of business management courses and from one of the two partners.

6. **What is your business mantra?**

Transparency, honesty, and mutual respect; good work life balance for all staff.

7. **What is a typical day for you as a business owner?**

I currently have a three day week: two clinical; one spent in the office. I get in by 8.15am, walk round the hospital and greet everyone, check what's happening, check emails and then either go straight into clinical work (ops or consulting) or, if in the office, have meetings, phone calls and reading to attend to. I then finish at 6pm, or sometimes later.

8. **What challenges are unique to being a veterinary business owner, compared to simply being a vet in practice?**

Balancing clinical, business, financial aspects without losing touch with what you are trying to do overall for the patients and clients. Pressures of running a business whilst dealing with staff.

9. **Did you have any prior business training?**

No.

10. **Do you think that vet students and graduates should receive specific business training?**

Yes.

11. **Some in the profession are concerned by the 'threat' of the 'corporates' in veterinary. Do you think they have anything to worry about?**

Not if they are well run and maintain their individuality and place in the local community. It is important to maintain clinical quality and an excellent standard of client service.

12. What are the main advantages to owning your own clinic? What are the disadvantages or challenges?

The advantages, as I see them, are: I enjoy a three day week; you get to develop as you want and to a level that you want; and freedom. It can be stressful because of the overall responsibility and pressures such as dealing with staff. There are fewer guarantees compared with with being an employee. As boss, you also have the final word and it can be difficult to switch off.

13. What do you see as being the main challenges for the industry in the UK in the next five to ten years?

The increasing gap between first opinion and referral level. First opinion vets seem more wary of trying new or non routine surgery or big medical work ups. I am not sure where this will leave the patient/client if there is no/insufficient insurance cover and then how the insurance companies will deal with the increasingly large bills as they are already becoming very precise over claims submitted.

14. What do you see being the structure of the UK vet industry in the medium to long term?

Corporates will continue to grow but not take over the profession. There will be more niche practices but the jack of all trades vet will become rarer, even in small animal work. There will be cheap and cheerful or quality at a price but not spanning all in one practice. I also anticipate there being problems with partnerships as there are likely to be fewer risk takers about so less people will be looking at going by this route, with more 9-5 vets and less OOH (out of hours) responsibility.

15. **What advice would you give prospective vets with a particular interest in business?**

Communicate your interest to your employers, learn from vets actually doing it as well as undertaking CPD, and continue to develop your skills. Look at all business and learn from other professions and service industries.

16. **What general advice would you offer students considering a career in veterinary?**

Be aware that a lot of it is routine and repetitive, but you will get out of it what you put in in terms of effort and enthusiasm. Enjoy people and communication.

17. **Do you see the course becoming more specialised?**

I hope not because people can't really choose exactly what area of veterinary they would like to commit to until they have experienced everything, although they probably will think they can! I always thought I would be a large animal vet until I found my niche in small animal.

18. **Some argue that it is impossible to be both a great clinician and a successful business owner. What would your response be?**

No, one doesn't negate the other. It's how you apply yourself that matters.

19. **What are your main clinical interests?**

Surgery of any kind and diagnostic imaging, plus scoping.

20. **What do you see as a the future for privately owned practices, such as yours?**

Pretty good as long as we keep on the ball and can adapt quickly to the clients/patients' needs. As a smaller more adaptable unit we can more easily guarantee a good quality of care and service.

21. **Do you have any pets?**

Yes. Two cats (Pippy, a pyscho-cat from Hell, and Lulu, who is nice but dim), a house tortoise (Tiddles), four ex-battery hens and a range of Cat Protection foster cats, who are penned outside.

VET SCHOOL

4: CAREER OPTIONS

Many of us have a picture in our mind of the traditional vet. The truth is that the classic idea of the 'Vet In Practice' is a very small part of the overall make-up of the profession, with a huge variety of different career options open to graduates and vets working in all fields and sectors of both the economy and society. Here, we explore some of the options open to graduates from the UK vet schools, and indeed veterinary on the whole.

Clinical Work

First Opinion

It is still very much the case that approximately 80% of new vets enter clinical practice, predominantly first-opinion, with this representing the classic 'GP' style of veterinary medicine in which vets advise owners on routine preventative measures, including procedures such as vaccination, neutering and dentals. They also see sick animals for the first time, using their knowledge, skills and clinical equipment and tests to diagnose and, where possible, treat cases. Although it used to be the case that most practices were mixed, meaning their vets saw both small animals and large animals, including horses and farm stock, it is becoming harder and harder to find genuinely mixed jobs these days, with a definite shift towards vets either treating large or small animals. The differentiation gets more specific still, with many large animal vets dealing with either just horses or farm animals. The 'mixed' jobs that are available tend to be in the more remote parts of the country and more often than not, the 'mix' is anything but, with a classic complaint from new vets being that the only large animal work they get to see is either TB testing or the occasional early morning emergency farm call-out. Neither of these really do much to foster an ongoing love for large animal work and these vets often find themselves making the decision to specialise and focus on either large or small animals, with many choosing the latter.

First opinion work enables vets to consolidate and develop their skills and knowledge across all of the disciplines, from medicine to surgery, including honing their expertise in the use of diagnostics such as radiography (using xrays), ultrasonography and other such tests. Although UK veterinary graduates are trained to achieve a basic level of 'Day One' competency and are, essentially, omni-competent, the truth is that the biggest learning curve usually occurs during those first few vital months in practice, during which new vets are exposed to cases which they have to manage on their own, without the safety net of knowing that the ultimate responsibility for their patient belongs to someone else. This is an incredibly daunting period and making sure that you choose a good practice that is going to a) support you during this incredibly important transition, and b) provide the opportunity to gain exposure to a broad range of cases and work them up thoroughly and effectively, is a vital thing to get right. The worst type of first practice would be one that expects a new graduate to manage a clinic on their own, with no positive input or guidance from senior vets. This is a sure way to reinforce potentially bad habits, many of which the new graduate will not even realise they have. Now that we have the Professional Development Phase (PDP), there is at least a basic framework for new graduates to follow in order to achieve the first target of 'Year One' competency, although this does still rely heavily on working in a practice that buys into the principle of the scheme as well as your own individual motivation.

First opinion work exposes new graduates to the following aspects of clinical veterinary work:

a) **Client contact** – As this book has reiterated many times, veterinary is a very people-centred profession and you will have to communicate and deal with a whole range of different people, from the plain crazy to the owners who are emotional and may, at times, be angry, confused, upset, elated, and all the emotions in between. You will learn the art of consulting and history taking, and be expected to manage client expectations, including ensuring clients are given accurate estimates and kept informed of changes to their animal's case, such as reporting results or discussing diagnoses and treatment options. The best way to get a feel for this is to watch qualified vets in action – you'll soon notice how they handle various different situations.

b) **Time pressure** – Chances are that at vet school you will have had the chance to take your own consults, although you probably would have been able to go over the usual 10-15 minute time limit that most veterinary consults last without too much incident. Once you're in private practice and working as a fresh-faced new vet you will be expected to be able to manage your time effectively and conduct consultations in the allotted time given. This rings equally true for routine surgeries, such as neutering, especially when you acknowledge the fact that 'time equals money' and the longer you take to do something, the less you can realistically do in any day and therefore the lower your earning potential for the practice. Now, no one is implying that all practices care about is how much money you can bring into the practice but it is important to realise early on that if the practice doesn't make money then they can't pay you, let alone consider investing in new equipment and facilities to enable them to develop. Its also important to be able to manage your time effectively from a personal welfare point of view. If you take ages with every consult, then the result will be that you end up regularly running over into lunch and your evenings, or having to start work earlier to enable you to deal with in-patients and the like. Vets work long hours at the best of times and if you end up making your days longer than they need to be then you'll end up stressed, ill and disillusioned, which would be no good to you or your practice.

c) **Money** – This makes practices function and you are employed to generate it, whilst also ensuring you fulfil your veterinary oath to uphold animal welfare. As such, you will learn the importance of charging correctly for your work, estimating so that clients are informed of the likely cost of tests and treatments before they are given the bill, and dealing with such matters as insurance claims. Unfortunately, it is a fact of life that a large proportion of complaints originate from disagreements about money, either because an owner wasn't prepared for how much their animal's care costs or for other similar reasons. It is important to have an appreciation and understanding of practice economics and to know the reasons for why vets charge what they do. It is also vital that you realise and recognise your own worth. You will have trained for at least five years to be a vet so it is only fair that you are paid a reasonable salary for a professional, and that the practice asks you to generate a certain amount of revenue to justify that salary. In turn, the practice must therefore charge accordingly to enable it to cover the myriad costs associated with running an average veterinary practice, pay you and also have money to be able to reinvest and develop the practice and the service offered to clients. It is great to see that many of the vet schools are introducing aspects of business studies into their undergraduate curriculum, thus equipping graduates with the knowledge and awareness of practice finance that they will need in their jobs. The other aspect of 'money awareness' which is important to learn in practice is the fact that sometimes, in spite of knowing what tests and treatments would have a good chance of making a difference in a specific case, cost can be the ultimate deciding factor in clients' decision-making. There is often very little way round this and it is up to you, as a vet, to discuss all of the options, from the cheapest right the way through to the 'Gold Standard,' with any client and allow them to ultimately make an informed decision.

d) **On-Call & Weekends** – Unless you're very lucky (and we will discuss whether it really is 'lucky') then you will be expected to do your fair share of weekend work and on-call. I have, for example, worked in clinics where I would see normal consults on a Saturday morning every four weeks or so, and then be on-call for a full weekend about every seven weeks. Each vet would also do one night on-call during the week, which was often quiet but could sometimes prove to be very busy indeed! Missed lunches, late finishes and nights with less-than-optimal amounts of sleep are all aspects of being a vet, which it is important to be prepared for if you wish to enter clinical practice. With the development and growth of emergency service providers, such as Vets Now, which cover out-of-hours (OOH) for practices, more and more first opinion jobs are able to offer their vets 'no out-of-hours.' Now, this may sound like a wonderful idea, and, trust me, it is, especially when you get to leave work at the end of the day and know that you don't have to worry about anything until the following day, but there are drawbacks to this 'perk,' especially if you are a new graduate. A lot of the more interesting and challenging cases in practice come to us rota then you would not get to see such cases, potentially limiting your clinical development and, also, the opportunity to manage cases and make clinical decisions yourself, without the all too reliable and convenient back-up of the senior vet in the next room. It is during these moments that new vets often feel themselves develop the most, as they are forced to 'step up to the mark.' Naturally, if you really did need assistance or advice on something out-of-hours then any good practice would have a system in place to enable you to contact a colleague. My first job was in a clinic that had no OOH and although the lack of sleepless nights was blissful, I became acutely aware upon joining my most recent UK practice of how underdeveloped my skills were in certain areas. Too much on-call, however, can be just as bad as it often leads to rapid burnout and sky-high stress levels. Not good.

e) **Continued Professional Development (CPD)** – All vets have to satisfy the RCVS that they continue to keep their knowledge and skills current and CPD is the way to ensure this. Vets are expected to complete a minimum of 135 hours of CPD over any three year period, with the PDP serving as new vets' first year of CPD. There are many forms that CPD can take, from attending conferences, such as the BSAVA Congress, company-sponsored meetings and lectures, which are often free, and courses run by commercial CPD providers and the universities. You are also allowed to record a certain number of hours of personal, private study and reading as CPD, and in-house professional development, for example, a colleague tutoring you and others how to get the best out of the ultrasound scanner for heart scans, can also count as CPD. Veterinary is very much a life-long commitment to learning and whether you choose to formalise and record this learning by sitting exams and achieving additional qualifications, or are happy to simply add to your knowledge and skill base, you will continue to develop right the way through your career.

Types of First Opinion Practice:

1. **'Traditional' Partnerships** – This is probably the classic model of veterinary ownership, with two or more people (not necessarily vets) owning an equal share of the business and thus being eligible to share in the profits. There are pros and cons associated with entering into a partnership arrangement, with one of the main cons being the huge expense that's normally involved in doing so. Although the level of commitment involved is huge, the perks can be great, including the ability to actually have a real input in to the running and development of the practice, and the fact that you can pay yourself a larger salary than you would be able to expect as a normal, salaried employee. It is my general impression that the average practice partner can expect a salary close to about £60,000 per year, although

this can obviously vary enormously depending on many factors.

2. **Limited Companies & 'Corporates'** – Many practice owners choose to go down the incorporation route rather than partnership, and there are, again, pros and cons of adopting this structure. Rather than being a 'partner', owners (shareholders) of a company are 'directors', and can pay themselves a salary, pay out a dividend from the profits, or a combination of the two. This is, understandably, the form that many of the 'Corporate' practices, such as CVS Plc, which is actually a publicly owned company with shares floated on the stock market, adopt. One important role that larger, corporate veterinary groups serve is to provide an exit strategy for practice owners, with less and less opportunity to bring in new partners owing to the changing demographic of the profession and the huge financial commitment required to do so. Companies such as CVS are able to buy practices, providing owners with a return on their original investment, and many former owners actually stay on to continue working at their practices, although without the stress associated with being the boss.

3. **Franchises** – Some practices, such as Vets4Pets, operate on a franchise basis, with practices being individually 'owned' by someone, who invests a certain amount of money into the practice, and the remainder of the seed capital being provided by the franchising company. The practice then trades under a common name, has similar clinic

appearances, equipment and drug and supplies lists, and has many of it's 'back office' functions, such as human resources and marketing, handled centrally by 'head office.' The advantage of this model is that vets are able to own their own practice and benefit directly from any profits and increase in value of the clinic, whilst also allowing them to commit more of their time to clinical work rather than the administrative duties normally associated with running a business.

Specialist Practice

There are an increasing number of practices offering specialist veterinary services, and these can either be the classic multi-disciplinary referral practice, such as Davies Veterinary Specialists in Hertfordshire, who see difficult and challenging cases from first opinion practices when they have exhausted their diagnostic and/ or treatment capabilities and knowledge, to the practices which specialise in either a single discipline, such as veterinary cardiology or ophthalmology, or a single species, such as The Cat Clinic in Oxford, or practices that just see exotics. Even the emergency clinics, such as Vets Now, which provides OOH cover for practices, represent a specialism, with the level of expertise in managing emergency cases – a truly fast-paced and exciting area of veterinary – extremely high and continuing to develop at a fantastic pace. The rate at which veterinary knowledge and expertise has developed over the past ten to twenty years, coupled with the increased importance of pet insurance, means that we are able to offer a far greater range of diagnostic and treatment options to owners and their animals than we ever used to be. From sophisticated cancer treatments to complex and ground-breaking orthopaedic surgical procedures, the services on offer to clients at most referral centres, both private and university-based, are ones that can rival those available in any NHS or private hospital.

Veterinary specialists study for additional qualifications, principally the diplomas bestowed by both the American and European Colleges of Veterinary Medicine, and complete their training in a specific field, such as small animal internal medicine or equine surgery. The training is rigorous and standards extremely high, with the status of 'specialist' not one that is easily applied. As with any vet, specialists have to show evidence of continued professional development in order to maintain their specialist status. See below for more information on specialist training.

1. **Internships** – These are usually one year paid placements, although the level of pay is normally relatively low, in which interns are exposed to referral cases, shadowing and learning from both residents and specialists in a particular field, such as small animal medicine. Many interns choose to then go on to complete residencies and train as specialists. A number of private practices offer internships, although most programmes are run by the vet schools. Its probably better, if you are interested in potentially pursuing a career as a specialist, to consider completing an internship

straight after finishing university. This is for a couple of reasons: a) you will be in a good position to build upon the veterinary knowledge you have after 5-6 years at university and will still be in the 'academic' frame of mind; and b) you won't notice the fact that internships are relatively poorly paid, especially compared to salaries in private practice. I would imagine it is a lot harder to effectively take a pay cut to return to university to complete an internship once you've had the taste of earning a good salary than it would be to go from earning nothing as a student to earning something as an intern. That may, however, simply be my own personal opinion and if you have the drive and desire to complete an internship then you will likely be prepared to make this sacrifice.

2. **Residencies** – These are normally three to four years in length and candidates usually work towards sitting their diploma exams at the end, thus achieving specialist status. Residencies are overseen and run by, or in conjunction with, universities and candidates are expected to have either completed an internship or to have equivalent clinical experience. This means that you could, in principle, become a resident after working in practice for a few years without having to complete an internship. Examples of residencies run by private practices but in conjunction with a university are the residency programmes at Dick White Referrals, which are run in conjunction with Nottingham University. Residents take on their own referral cases, work closely with

and learn from diploma holders, undertake research and teach undergraduates as part of their programme. They are hard work and not for the faint-hearted, but if you have an ambition to become a specialist then they are certainly the path to follow.

3. **CertAVP and other certificates** – These are professional qualifications, which are designed to be studied for, and completed by vets in clinical practice. The new CertAVP (Certificate in Advanced Veterinary Practice), awarded by the RCVS, replaces the old certification system and has been running for several years now. Candidates have the option of registering for a general certificate or to sign up to study towards a certificate with a specific focus, such as small animal surgery. This difference only becomes apparent during the latter stages of the certificate training and also in the way some of the assessment is conducted. Candidates have to have completed their PDP after graduation, and then to register with the RCVS to be eligible to study for the certificate. You get a maximum of ten years in which to complete the certificate and have to renew your registration each year until you finish it. Once you have registered with the RCVS you then need to choose a university or college through which study. There are a number of institutions that administer the certificate, including vet schools such as the RVC in London, and once you have signed up with one of them the fun begins. For many, studying for a certificate provides a welcome challenge

and structure to their work as vets in general, first opinion practice, and they are more than happy to develop skills and expertise in all areas of their clinical work, whereas others use a certificate as a launch-pad into further, specialist training such as those already discussed.

Out of Hours Veterinary

Whilst it used to be the case that emergency and out-of-hours clinical work was something you were expected to do as part of your regular vet 'day job,' this has changed significantly over the years. Out-of-hours work now represents a specific career path and specialism, with many vets working solely in this sector. There are a number of emergency cover providers, of varying sizes, with the main player being Vets Now, who provide out-of-hours cover for scores of clinics. Many vets elect to work solely as out-of-hours vets, focusing their training and energies on effectively becoming emergency specialists. The advantages include an exciting 'anything can happen' nature to your clinical work, to being free to work on your own, or with a much smaller number of people than you might in general day practice, and to start and end your working day when most others are finishing and starting theirs respectively. Most out-of-hours jobs involve working a run of nights in a row, with several days off, meaning that if you can cope with this unconventional working pattern, there is time available to indulge in other activities, such as travelling. I am aware of some emergency vets, for example, who will work seven days and then have one to two weeks off enabling them to go off travelling or even live overseas.

Non-Clinical Careers

To think that vets only ever work in a clinical capacity would be to miss the bigger picture and although the vast majority of vets are engaged in some form of clinical practice, there are many other positions and careers that vets are able to thrive in. Examples include the following:

a) **Government & State positions** – vets are vital to the safety and viability of the UK food supply and also to our general bio-security. From working as an Official Veterinarian inspecting animals and meat in abattoirs, to carrying out TB testing on cattle for DEFRA, vets play a pivotal role in ensuring the health of the nation. Vets are also active at ports and airports, overseeing the import and export of animals and animal-related goods, both legal and illegal. There are numerous opportunities for vets to make a real difference in disease surveillance by working for the Veterinary Laboratories Agency (VLA). Other important government work includes roles within Animal Health, the agency formerly known as the State Veterinary Service, and as Home Office Inspectors. Having some knowledge of the variety of such important roles that vets play may impress interviewers if you are asked about them.

b) **Business** – numerous vets work within the sales, marketing and technical teams of pharmaceutical and neutraceutical companies, to name but a few, and use the vast range of skills that they have developed during their training and work, both clinical and non-clinical, to help develop new products, sell them to veterinary customers and help them understand and use them effectively and safely. Potential attractions of swapping a scrub top for a business suit include generally more reliable and sociable working hours (ie more of a '9-to-5' schedule), opportunities to travel, and, perhaps, more money depending on the role.

c) **Biomedical Industry** – there are many vets engaged in the research and development of new treatments for both human and veterinary markets. They may, for example, be employed as a named veterinary surgeon, for the purpose of engaging in research using animals, or for their expertise in specific disciplines, such as pathology. As with clinical practice, the opportunities to specialise are many and some vets even opt to head down the executive career path, working in management positions and playing a direct role in building and running such companies.

d) **The Armed Forces** – vets can join the Army as part of the Royal Army Veterinary Corp (RAVC), entering as captains for a four year Short Service Commission. This may then be altered to a regular commission on application. The Army also offer sponsorship in the form of bursaries and cadetships to students studying veterinary medicine, although the minimum service period is a year longer. The attractions of a career with the RAVC include the ability to travel, develop excellent leadership skills and engage in interesting and varied veterinary work, including the opportunity to study for further qualifications, especially the CertAVP.

e) **Charity** – there are lots of opportunities for vets to become involved in charitable work for a range of organisations. This may involve salaried positions with charities such as the PDSA, Dogs Trust and RSPCA, providing veterinary care in much the same manner as normal veterinary practice, to unpaid, voluntary work for charities such as the Worldwide Veterinary Service (www.wvs.org.uk), offering the chance to make a difference as a vet in many parts of the world.

f) **Academia, Research & Teaching** – many veterinary graduates enter academia, for example through studying for a PhD, and are engaged in conducting original research as well as teaching. Many residents also have teaching duties, which may involve both lecturing to undergraduates and conducting tutorials.

g) **Complete Change** – at this stage the idea of not working within veterinary may seem like an impossible one but the truth is that a proportion of vets will, at some stage during their careers, opt to change career altogether and for a variety of different reasons. These may range from disillusionment with the long hours, pressure and relatively low reward to lifestyle considerations, such as the desire to find a job that fits in more with raising a young family. Some vets simply wish to find a new challenge and don't see that veterinary can offer them what they are seeking anymore. The types of career that veterinary graduates might find themselves in are many, owing to the fact that vets possess a huge range of transferrable skills which make them highly employable across many sectors, from banking and finance to, well, anything really. Even writing books!

Opportunity to Travel

A degree in veterinary medicine is a passport to the rest of the world, especially if you graduate from either a US or a UK vet school. With a UK degree many countries, including Australia and New Zealand, allow you to travel to and work as a vet without sitting additional exams, which is fantastic. If you wish to work in America then you will need to pass both the national board exams and any exams that the specific state in which you plan to work requires you to sit. These exams are tough, include everything that you would have needed to study for your final degree exams, and are also expensive to sit, with no guarantee of passing. If you attend a UK vet school which has AVMA

(American Veterinary Medical Association) accreditation then you do not have to sit the national board exams, just the state exams. It seems that the best time, in my opinion, to sit the American board exams is about the same time as you are studying for your finals, as the level of knowledge you are likely to have is as broad and developed as it is ever going to be. Going back and studying cattle reproduction, for example, after five years in small animal practice might not be the easiest thing in the world to do! Another option, which some UK veterinary graduates take, including good friends of mine, is to apply for and complete an internship in the US, during which you are usually prepared well for the national and state exams. For those of you dedicated enough to gain accreditation to work in America, the rewards include a higher salary than you could expect as a vet in the UK, and the weird feeling of everyone calling you "doctor," as vets are referred to as doctors in the US.

Whichever country you do plan to travel to and work in, it is always recommended to contact the embassy of the country in question to check visa requirements and other such details. It would be easy to fill a hundred more pages with amazing stories and profiles of vets who are working in far-flung parts of the globe, whether it be working with cowboys in Colorado, treating racehorses for Sheikhs in Saudi Arabia, or working in small animal first opinion practice in Australia. The possibilities are endless and if it's a profession that offers you the chance to travel widely and support yourself doing an interesting and varied job then veterinary may be just what you're looking for! In fact, at the time of writing this I am preparing to move to the United Arab Emirates in order to work in small animal practice in Dubai, meaning that by the time you read this I will be practicing what I preach by working overseas. Get in touch and come and say hi if you find yourself over there.

SUMMARY

There are a huge variety of opportunities open to veterinary graduates and a career in traditional clinical practice is not the only path there is to tread. Vets work across a range of sectors and industries, and in a plethora of roles. Employment prospects still remain good and with any luck this will remain so.

Lucy Chadwick
MVB MRCVS
Marketing & Business Development Manager, & In-House Veterinary Surgeon
Pet Drugs Online
(www.petdrugsonline.co.uk)

I graduated from University College Dublin in 2009. I spent three years in Small Animal practice in the UK, both in permanent and locum roles before moving into veterinary industry. I am now the Marketing and Business Development Manager and in-house Veterinary Surgeon for Pet Drugs Online, an online veterinary dispensary based in Bath. I currently live in Chippenham, Wiltshire with my fiancé James and our Border Terrier Poirot. Outside of work I am on the BSAVA Southern Region Committee and sing in a chamber choir called Schola.

Alternative Career Path

1. When did you first decide that you wanted to be a vet?

I honestly can't remember ever wanting to be anything but a vet! I suppose the idea started around the age of 7. I was very into horse riding at that stage and was always very taken with working with animals. When I got into secondary school and found my talents lay in science it seemed like a natural fit.

2. What prompted you to make a change?

About halfway through vet school I realised that there were actually many more options for vets that the traditional practice route. I spent two summers on research scholarships in the UCD labs, which was fantastic, but I felt after that a life of laboratory based research was probably not for me. When I was in 4th year vet school I attended a talk given by Ciara Feeney, at that stage a Veterinary Technical Adviser for Intervet Ireland, and I became interested in finding out more our veterinary industry roles. I ended up shadowing Ciara for a week when I was in final year and decided that a career in veterinary industry was what I wanted to do. By researching job advertisements and talking to vets in the pharmaceutical industry I found that the general requirements included at least 3-5 years veterinary practice experience and well developed communication skills. I therefore spent three years in practice, while undertaking many extra-curricular activities, before applying for industry jobs.

3. What do you do in your current role?

My current job role is very varied! I oversee all marketing activities in the business, plan campaigns, liaise with manufacturers, source new product lines, create links with charities, provide technical support to our team of SQPs and management team, deal with regulatory and legislative requirements, oversee dispensing protocols, deal with customer queries, write a blog and newsletters and many other things!

I also recently developed and ran a successful PR campaign for the business about flea problems in pets which included being interviewed on BBC Radio 4 and BBC West Midlands Radio and being quoted in articles for the BBC News Magazine online, The Telegraph and The Daily Mail. I am also in charge of the social media for the business and this is something I really enjoy.

4. How did your veterinary training and experience help prepare you for your current role, and do you draw on your veterinary skills now?

I use my veterinary skills everyday as I am constantly responding to questions from my team about various medications and conditions. I also run a veterinary advice service through our website so I spend some time everyday dealing with customer queries; my experience of working in veterinary practice is invaluable for this. I will say that we received zero training in communication and business skills while in vet school so I have had to actively find opportunities to gain this knowledge after qualifying.

5. What do you most enjoy about your job?

I love the variety. Every day is different and there is a lot more variety than in general practice. I like being able to plan my own working day and decide which projects I wish to tackle first. I also enjoy the customer facing side of the role; daily interaction with clients keeps my veterinary skills fresh.

6. What are the main challenges associated with your current job?

There has been a steep learning curve since coming from practice. There is also the challenge of balancing profitability and keeping within all relevant legislation. It is a very fast moving industry so I need to keep on top of any changes.

7. How did friends and family respond when you decided that you wanted a career change?

My family and friends always knew this was the path I wanted to follow so they were very supportive and happy for me. I found It was generally other vets I did not know so well who gave me a hard time, suggesting that I couldn't "hack" practice or accusing me of damaging the profession by going to work for an online veterinary dispensary. At least we are veterinary owned and run, unlike many which are pharmacy owned, therefore the revenue we produce stays within the veterinary sector.

8. Do you ever miss clinical veterinary?

I still spend the odd day providing holiday and sick cover in some of the practices owned by the business. I find this is more than enough to keep my hand in! Even if I was to leave it behind completely I don't think I would miss it.

9. Where do you see yourself in five years? Ten years?

I would hope to have progressed to a more senior managerial role within the industry. I am just finishing up a GPCertificate in Veterinary Business and Management. I would hope to undertake a Diploma in Marketing in the next few years. Longer term I would like to undertake an MBA (finances allowing!).

10. What advice would you offer to someone considering applying to vet school?

Be really sure you want to do it before applying! You need to be very aware of the realities (both financial and lifestyle) of being a vet. The media often glamourise the job of being a vet, so it is important to see the realities by seeing practice and talking to as many vets as you can. You will likely end up with a large student debt from doing the course, have a look at salary surveys to see if the actual expected salary will be enough to pay this off in the time frame that you require. You may be surprised at how low salaries actually are for vets!

11. Any additional information that you would like to add?

For anyone considering a career such as mine it is important to realise it is not something good to do when you are fed up with practice! The people who tend to do well in the industry see it as something they have wanted to do for a long time and have built up the relevant skills. If you are interested I would advise talking to as many reps and technical advisors as you can, and if possible undertake some work experience. Also spend time building up relevant extra-curricular activities e.g. by doing presentations or writing articles. These develop the sort of skills they generally look for. Keep on top of what is going on in the industry by regularly reading veterinary press. It is important to know which companies are being bought out and what new products are coming on the market, these could spell employment opportunities so keep your eyes open.

Also I would advise that all Vet Students and Vet Graduates get involved with the veterinary societies e.g. the British Veterinary Association, Veterinary Ireland and the British Small Animal Veterinary Society to name just a few. Many of these offer free or heavily discounted rates for students. They are great for providing regular journals and running CPD events, from regional events to large congresses. By getting involved you will get to meet a large cross section of the profession, which can be useful when you are looking for support or jobs later on! When I moved from my first to my second job I ended up moving over 300 miles and didn't know anyone. I got involved in the BSAVA Southern Region Committee where I currently serve as Communications Officer and acting Treasurer. This has been very rewarding and I have met some great people.

Emma Trantham
BSc BVSc MRCVS
PhD Student
University of Bristol

I graduated in 2009 from the University of Bristol having taken a year out to get my intercalated degree in Veterinary Pathogenesis (also at the University of Bristol). I'm currently a third year PhD student (still at the University of Bristol) researching how the food poisoning bacterium *Campylobacter jejuni* colonises chickens. This means that I don't really have a set routine day to day as it depends on what experiments I am running. Most days I will have lab work: whether that's plating out chicken poo samples, counting bacteria or multiplying up DNA depends on what needs doing at the time. I also spend time reading research articles and analysing my results back in the office. Away from work I love singing and am a member of several choirs. I have also recently bought two young pet rats so currently spend a lot of time training them.

Veterinary Research

1. When did you first develop an interest in veterinary research?

I first considered research as a career during my preclinical years of vet school. I did a summer research project and that inspired me to intercalate – basically take a year out to complete the 3rd year of a science degree – in Veterinary Pathogenesis. The research project I carried out during my intercalated year and the project I completed at the University of Cambridge's Fundamentals of Veterinary Science Summer School made me think even more about pursuing research as a career.

2. Can you describe your career progression to date? Where do you see yourself in five years? Ten years?

I graduated in 2009 and after a (very) short stint locuming in practice I took up a research assistant post in my current lab while applying for my PhD. I started my PhD in October 2010 and haven't looked back since! I hope to finish my PhD by October 2013 (assuming all my experiments go to plan...). As to what I want to do after that – I haven't fully decided yet. I would like to have a career that involves research, but I don't think I want that to be my whole career. I really enjoyed pathology at university so have been considering applying for a residency in that. At the moment it's quite hard to think about the future – I'm mostly focussed on getting my PhD finished!

3. What role do vets play in furthering scientific understanding and progress?

Vets play a very important role in scientific research and discovery, whether it is in the 'basic science' fields or in more clinical research. The training vet school gives vets means that they have a broad biology knowledge base and have already learnt how to logically approach a problem. Obviously veterinary training is incredibly useful when involved in clinical research involving animals.

4. How aware were you of research as a career option when you were both applying to vet school and during your training?

I don't think I was really that aware of research as a career option when I started university. Exposure to researchers as I went through university did increase my awareness but it wasn't until I actively started looking into it as a career (during summer projects and intercalation) that I realised it was more common than I had thought.

5. How can more vets be encouraged into veterinary research?

I'm not sure I really know how best to encourage more vets to consider research as a career. Speaking for myself I think more visibility of researchers (including seeing more of the research that the clinicians who lectured us were doing) would have been helpful. Information on the pathways to a research career and how research careers can progress would also have been more useful.

6. What do you most enjoy about undertaking original, scientific research?

I love the moment when I get the results from an experiment and I am the first person to know that particular thing about the organism or disease I am working on (admittedly it is usually something very tiny but it is still pretty exciting).

7. What are the main challenges associated with being a veterinary researcher?

I'm still very early on in my research career so I can't speak for the challenges later on in a research career path, but when I started my PhD the main difficulty was that it often felt like my supervisors and colleagues expected me to have the same level of knowledge as someone who had done a microbiology degree – whilst I had done microbiology on the vet course it was mostly clinical and a lot of the basic stuff was skirted over. I think the biggest challenge I will face post-PhD is job-hunting. Post-PhD jobs are a bit thin on the ground at the moment and so will probably involve me moving away from the South West.

8. If you could sum up veterinary research in five words, what would they be?

Exciting; challenging; fun; learning; inspiring.

9. Do you still undertake clinical veterinary work? If not, do you miss being a practical clinician?

I don't undertake any clinical veterinary work. I do miss it sometimes, especially some of the clients, but not so much that I necessarily want to go back to it.

10. What advice would you offer someone considering a career in veterinary research?

If you are thinking about pursuing a career in veterinary research try to get a holiday placement in a lab doing a specific project – it will give you a small taster as to what research is like. While a vet student consider intercalating as that will give you more research experience and will also help down the line if you do then decide to pursue a research career. Finally, have a look round at different vets in research – some work in the more lab-based 'basic' science areas, some are much more clinically based. It's important to remember that there are lots of different aspects of veterinary research so even if you do a project in one area and don't like it there may well be another one that you would enjoy.

11. What general advice would you offer to someone considering becoming a vet?

I'm sure others will have more useful information about how to go about getting into vet school than I have. I guess my main advice would be to remember that going to vet school doesn't necessarily mean you will end up as a vet in clinical practice. There are lots of other jobs where a vet degree is a great help.

Dr Dave Nicol

BVMS Cert Mgmt MRCVS

Director, North Ryde Veterinary
Hospital Sydney, Australia

Dr Dave Nicol is a practicing veterinarian and owns an A-class
Veterinary Hospital in Sydney. Before moving to Australia he was
head vet and business development director with Parkvets Ltd (UK)
and has worked as a consultant to some of the UKs largest veterinary
groups. He writes business articles for My Exceptional Veterinary
Team, The Veterinary Business Journal and Veterinary Economics
and is a popular presenter at veterinary conferences around the
world. Dave graduated from Glasgow University Veterinary School in
1998. You can follow him on Twitter at www.twitter.com/drdavenicol
or read his management blog at www.davenicol.com/blog.

Entrepreneurial Vet

1.When did you first decide you wanted to be a vet? Why?

I wanted to do something that had a strong tie to the community, my
father lectured medical students and I lived in rural Scotland next to a
farm so animal contact and medicine was pretty much always there.

Like any young man I wanted to be an astronaut, fighter pilot and a range of other weird and wonderful things. I think when I finally said something sensible; my parents jumped on it and breathed a sigh of relief more than anything else!

2. Have you always wanted to start your own business? What prompted you to do so?

Even as a kid I had business savvy, I used to publish a magazine for the other kids in my village and fix up their broken skateboards for money. When my mum found out though, she went nuts! My family were pretty socialist so such capitalist instincts were not terribly well tolerated. Like most other people who start their own businesses I have a great deal of ideas, self-belief and motivation. It was great working for some amazing people through my career, but it was also inevitable that I run my own veterinary businesses eventually.

3. How did you get involved with your current entrepreneurial endeavour?

I was working in a senior role in a large practice in London, but I had planned to take a year out in the sun before settling into "real life". Australia is a pretty amazing place and as the time to leave beckoned my wife and I made the decision to stay. From that moment onward there was only going to be one way for me, open up my own practice and charge forward. The 18 months since I would describe as the best of my career. It's been a lot of hard work, but an immense amount of fun too.

4.Have you, in your opinion, always been entrepreneurial? What does that word mean to you?

I think so, for me entrepreneurs see the world in a different way, or have a desire to change it. So vision is a hugely important part of being an entrepreneur. But more than anything, I associate the word with freedom. Not that you are free from responsibility, far from it. If anything you have more responsibilities. But you are your own boss, and as such, you are free to shape your future the way you see fit.

5.What are the main advantages associated with being your own boss/ starting and running your own business?

You are in the position to create your own future, build a service in the way you think best and take charge of your life. This is massively energising and also (if you set things up right) provides great flexibility as you can chose what times you want to work.

6.What are the main challenges?

Being present at work and at home. Letting go of the reigns as the business starts to grow. Lots of people can start small businesses, but if you are successful and your business grows, you have to able to trust other people take on a lot of the work you once did yourself. For an entrepreneur this can be really challenging.

7. What are the three key lessons that you have learnt since starting in business and that you would pass on to the next generation of entrepreneurs?

Don't be afraid to screw things up, the path to success is most definitely not a straight line!

When you do screw things up, learn from the mistake and do things better next time.

Embrace change, for it will surely embrace you.

8. What do you see as being the big opportunities and the big threats faced by the veterinary profession at present?

The opportunities and threats are largely the same thing, just viewed through different lenses. For example, the huge over supply of undergraduates that is beginning to happen is terrible news for young vets, but great news for employers.

The Internet has only really started to disrupt our market, expect this to worsen. The new economic reality will be a feature of life for a long time.

We are being squeezed from all sides and need to wise up as a profession to business to continue to thrive.

9.What are the key skills or attributes you need to have or develop in order to thrive as a veterinary entrepreneur?

A willingness to take risks.

A passion for making something better.

A reality check that you probably won't make millions in the process.

10. Give a detailed description of the work that you do. What are your job responsibilities?

I try really hard to make people with pets happy. End of.

11. Describe your first day as a new business owner. What was the experience like? Are there any interesting anecdotes that you would like to share?

It was an exhausting day, mostly it went well, but we had our fair share of dramas. We didn't make enough money, stuff broke and I had a splitting headache. But we had great fun and I was certain that day two would be even better than day one.

12. What challenges did you encounter on your first day? What challenges do you encounter now?

The internet broke and my systems are all cloud based! Which made sure we had back up in place before things got to messy. We went live with a new price list, new boss and new computer system one day one.

In spite of the training, the team weren't sure which way to go. We got muddled heaps, but it was all taken in good spirits by our customers. I also cannot stand administrative tasks, I'd always had people to do this bit for me. So here I was tea boy, banker, salesman, mentor, vet, cleaner, receptionist....a long list for one day!

The business has grown well and now greatest challenge for me is finding and managing good people.

13. What is the hardest part of your job and why?

Dealing with people, that's the hardest job of all. It takes different strokes to inspire and manage different folks, being that person to everyone takes a lot of time and energy. But it's worth the hard work.

14. What fulfillment do you get from your job?

I get enormous reward from seeing my dreams and vision come to life. I also still love being a vet, meeting people and building relationships.

15. What lessons have you learned through establishing your company?

Get the best help doing it that you can afford.

16. What do you think helped you in your success?

Experience, passion and savvy. I learned from all the business efforts I messed up before this one!

17. Where and how do you see yourself five or ten years from now?

I see myself having fun whatever. That's the promise I made myself, to always be doing something I enjoy. So that might mean running veterinary practices or it might mean something completely different.

18. What advice can you give to others so that they too can tread the path of the entrepreneur and make their millions?

Don't do it to make milllons! At least you won't be disappointed.

19. Do you think that entrepreneurship and/ or business skills should be taught more widely at vet school?

No, that will just increase my competition! More seriously, yes. Absolutely. We should certainly get more communication skills from people who have been there and done it for real.

20. How do you support future veterinary entrepreneurs and is there any support that you wish had been available when you were starting out?

I write a veterinary management blog called the hamster wheel, host a large veterinary management group online and travel the world speaking at conferences about my experiences in management. I also run Sydney's only first opinion small animal internship where I personally mentor a new graduate each year. Finally I give guest lectures to the students at Sydney University Veterinary School on business.

David Sajik
BVetMed MRCVS
Junior Clinical Training Scholar
The Queen Mother Animal

I graduated from The Royal Veterinary College in 2009. After graduation, I worked in a busy two-branch small animal practice before embarking on my quest to become a veterinary specialist. I did not always want to be a specialist; when I graduated, I was fully prepared to spend the rest of my career working in small animal general practice with the ambition of setting up my own facility.

Whilst working, I discovered my interest in surgery and from there made the decision to become a specialist. After my first job, I obtained a surgical internship at Fitzpatrick Referrals, a private orthopaedic referral centre, where my drive to become a specialist was confirmed, through working as part of an incredibly dedicated team. After completing my first internship, I moved back to The Royal Veterinary College to complete a rotating internship in the university referral hospital; here I have again had the chance to work as part of a world-leading team, experiencing life in the largest small animal referral hospital in Europe whilst expanding my knowledge and skill base extensively along the way.

Outside of work, I enjoy being outdoors and especially taking part in winter sports, although I have had little opportunity in the last couple of years. Specialising takes a high level of dedication, however

I believe it is vital to maintain work-life balance; it just takes a little more effort.

Specialist Training

1. **When did you first decide that you wanted to be a veterinary specialist? What prompted your decision?**

The decision to become a veterinary specialist was, for me, more of an evolution than a single, discrete decision or realisation.

Whilst at vet school on extra mural studies (EMS), I was fortunate to see practice in a busy small animal practice with an orthopaedic certificate holder. This practice was where I gained my first exposure to veterinary surgery of any kind, be it the day-to-day surgery common to any small animal veterinary practice in the UK, or the orthopaedic surgery with the certificate holder. I returned to this practice several times during my training, and was very privileged to see practice with a European and American board certified specialist in small animal surgery who had begun using the practice facilities as a base for her referral service. It was at this time that I realised I had an interest in surgery. However, at this point in my training, everything was new and exciting and I could see myself forging a career within almost any area of the veterinary field.

During my final year, I contemplated both applying for internships immediately after graduation and going into small animal or mixed practice. I really had no idea what I wanted to do; I had spent more than 10 years wanting to be a vet but, at this time, did not know what aspect of being a vet I found most appealing. Following graduation, I was offered a job working with one of the assistant vets from my EMS placement practice, who had left to set up her own practice. Whilst working there, I found that I really enjoyed every aspect of the day-to-day life of general practice; I developed my own group of clients and was pleased to be part of a very friendly and capable team. I found surgery particularly satisfying and was very fortunate to be part of a team that was keen to teach and pass on their skills to a new graduate. I think the realisation that I wanted to become a surgical specialist was borne initially out of frustration – I had spent 5 years learning what was possible but my capability was limiting the service I could offer. In practice, I found that I was being presented with surgical conditions for which I knew what was required for treatment, but was limited by my own ability and facilities available to me in general practice. It was incredibly frustrating to make a diagnosis but then have to refer the animal to someone else to fix. I have always had the drive to do the best I can. From this evolved my desire to become a specialist veterinary surgeon.

2. **What has been your career progression to date and what stages do you need to go through in order to qualify as a specialist?**

The term specialist is reserved for veterinary surgeons who have obtained a veterinary diploma in their particular field, usually accredited in the UK by the European, American or the Royal College of Veterinary Surgeons. Prior to being accepted onto a residency training program, many positions require the completion of a number of years in practice, often to include an RCVS/ECVS recognised internship. The specific training typically requires completion of a 3 or 4 year residency training programme, under the guidance of a boarded specialist, before sitting examinations; other criteria - including case log, publications and presentations - are also part of the residency training programme.

After graduation from the Royal Veterinary College I spent just under 18 months working in small animal general practice just outside Guildford, Surrey. During the final 6 months I used my half day to see practice at Fitzpatrick Referrals, a nearby orthopaedic referral centre, taking the opportunity to see referral orthopaedic surgery and gain further experience in a hospital environment. Then, when the opportunity arose I secured a 12 month position as an intern. After completing the internship I stayed an additional 2 months completing research studies I had undertaken, before returning to general practice as a locum vet; including some out-of-hours work. During this time I obtained my current position as a Junior Clinical Training Scholar (University internship) at the Royal Veterinary College, with the plan to apply for residency positions next year.

3. **What advice and information on options to specialise were available when you were at vet school? Do you think there was sufficient information provided?**

During the last two of years of my undergraduate training we had careers days when various aspects of 'life and work after vet school' were discussed, and when vets and people from research and industry were available to discuss options and career plans. Understandably, it was assumed that the majority of people in my year would move into general practice after graduation and, as a result, most of the career guidance was focused on this. There were students who knew already that they wanted to specialise, research or move into industry straight after graduation and, as far as I know, they were able to find the guidance they required within the university or as a result of help from members of staff with contacts in the relevant field.

4. **What is your opinion on the idea of introducing specialisation earlier in the vet course? Should vet undergraduates be given an opportunity to specialise before graduating or should we continue to graduate with skills and knowledge across the board?**

This is a difficult question to address and, obviously, I can only comment on my own personal experiences. I believe firmly that any veterinary specialisation should be built upon the foundation of a strong general veterinary knowledge base. If specialisation is to be introduced earlier in the veterinary course, I believe it should be by providing additional teaching but without compromising other very important areas.

During my degree, I was given ample opportunity to explore nearly every area of veterinary science. The final clinical year provided broad exposure to most aspects of veterinary practice; there was time in the university first opinion practice as well as EMS first opinion placements in conjunction with multiple weeks in the university referral hospital environment and weeks dedicated to veterinary research. The majority of students plan to move into general practice after graduation; however, offering additional teaching and tutoring to students keen to pursue specialist careers could be very beneficial to the early careers of these individuals.

5. **What is the biggest challenge associated with pursuing specialist training?**

Irrespective of the field in which you intend to specialise, competition for residency positions will be fierce. I have colleagues who have applied for every residency opening, year after year, and have not yet been successful; some have given up after years of trying. Some fields are more competitive than others, but obtaining a residency position in any field is a huge achievement and, from what I hear, is getting more highly contested each year.

The residencies themselves are intense; long hours at work, evenings and weekends studying, working on-call, research and publication requirements all mount up so commitment is vital to success. Once the residency has been completed, the final hurdle is the diploma examination – which has been described by a colleague as "the hardest exam you will ever sit".

6. **How long do you expect your training to become a specialist to take?**

The specialist training itself usually requires completion of a 3- or 4-year residency placement. Today, achieving a residency placement is the biggest challenge. Realistically, you should anticipate at least 4 to 5 years of post-graduate training before sitting the diploma examination. Having spent 2 years completing internships I am looking at a minimum of 5 years further training, but I could potentially spend the next 5 years (or longer) trying to get a residency position, whilst working in practice as a locum to support myself.

7. **What is a typical day for you, if such a day exists?**

The typical day of an intern is quite difficult to describe because there is such great variation between internships and also day-to-day within an internship.

In my first internship, interns were primarily assistants to the senior surgeons. This provided fantastic experience both in surgery and also pre- and post-surgery with case investigation, diagnostics and management. Knowledge and skills were obtained 'on the job' through clinical experience of referral cases. The typical day started between 8-9am, depending upon the shift, and extended until all the work was complete, often in the early hours of the following morning.

My current placement is a rotating internship, during which we spend time working with all the major services in the hospital, combined with manning the out-of-hours service, providing exposure to first opinion as well as referral cases. Again, the primary role is as an assistant to the senior clinicians. In the university environment, a key part of our job is working with the students, helping with organisation of procedures, case management and clinical discussions; these are additional facets of the job that I really enjoy.

8. **What do you most enjoy about your training?**

It is difficult to focus on one thing; I feel very fortunate to have worked in two highly progressive referral centres with many clinicians at the leading edge of their field. The internships have given me the opportunity to see what is possible in veterinary medicine alongside improving my general knowledge and ability through working closely with specialist professionals. Even if I am unsuccessful in my aim of becoming a surgical specialist, the skills and knowledge I will have gained through the internships should benefit my clinical practice, ultimately making me a better clinician.

9. **What do you least enjoy about your training?**

The path to specialising takes a high level of dedication; unfortunately, aspects of life outside of work do get pushed back. I have been very lucky to enjoy working in first opinion practice and two referral centres; I have been exposed to multiple aspects of the profession and have taken as much as I can from each experience. The hours are long and the work demanding but I cannot say that I have disliked anything about the past couple of years; they have been tough, but have facilitated greater experience and exposure and hopefully a better level of knowledge, understanding and capability.

10. **Many people think that you have to take a pretty big pay-cut when moving from practice into training on either an internship or residency. How true is that assumption?**

From my experience, it is true that payment during internships and residencies is significantly less than would be expected by a vet working in general practice. However, payment depends very much on the individual placement and practices often provide additional benefits such as accommodation and extensive CPD opportunities. Many universities pay a tax-free stipend and offer student status, whereas most private practices pay an annual salary. The annual salary appears to vary greatly between placements, so is something that should be looked at by applicants. Ultimately, the main benefit to be achieved through internships and residency programs is the further development of knowledge and case exposure.

11. **What advice would you give to a young vet wanting to specialise during their career?**

Becoming a specialist is not an easy task and, therefore, deciding to embark on specialist training is not a decision to be made on a whim or impulse. Interest in a specific subject area is a very good starting point; from there you need to do some research – whats, wheres, whens etc. I found that specialists and vets working in specialist or referral centres were a fantastic source of advice and guidance. My tutor in my final years at university was a very good source of advice for the immediate post-graduation period.

I have been very fortunate to work with a number of specialists during my internships, each offering their own advice. I recommend sourcing as many points of view and opinions as possible, and then use the collective advice to help you make your decisions. The ultimate answer is that there are no real 'hard and fast' answers to becoming a specialist – I have friends who have tried for years to obtain a residency position and been unsuccessful, and I have colleagues who have gone straight from university to internship and then residency.

Irrespective of your field of choice, competition for places is strong, either because many people want the subject or because certain subjects have very few places to offer each year – you have to stand out. Maximising your experience is a key factor, either through internships or further training such as CPD, certification, and further education such as BSc, MSc and PhD degrees. Presenting work and studies at veterinary meetings is a strong addition to your experience and may provide the opportunities to meet people already within the field of interest. Veterinary research and publications are an important part of the residency programme and being able to demonstrate an interest and a capability is a very important skill. The selection panel for residency positions has a very tough job working though a sea of applicants – if they have already met or worked with candidates, they will have a better insight into applications and this should help maximise chances of acceptance. Remember, the selection panel are choosing someone to work with for at least 3 years, it is best if they've met you first and that you have made a good impression. Visiting practices and institutions, attending veterinary meetings and CPD courses are ideal opportunities for this and, in addition, it will improve your CV.

There will always be many good applicants for residency positions; despite all the hard work applicants put in there is no doubt that luck has a part to play in many successful applications – either being in the right place at the right time, being asked the right questions at interview, or simply being given that little nugget of advice that edges you ahead of other applicants. I work on the principle that the harder you work the luckier you get. Play fair and no one can ask any more of you.

There is little more for me to say really – good luck and I look forward to potentially working with you in the future.

12. **Any additional information that you would like to add.**

At this time I have not looked outside the UK for residency positions. However, should I not succeed in obtaining a place in the UK, I would look to apply for programmes in America to maximise my chances.

Applications for internship and residency positions in North America work very differently to the UK. It is not unlike the UCAS university application process, in that all applications are processed centrally once a year. Most of the positions are applied for and awarded through the 'Veterinary Internship and Residency Matching Program' or the 'Match'. All information is available from www.virmp.org.

Institutions and private practices upload the details of available positions, with application requirements and program contents between September and October. From mid-October applicants are able to review programs and decide upon their rankings, with the application deadline in early December. The results of the Match are usually posted in February.

The prospective intern or resident selects the program or programs they wish to apply for and 'ranks' them in order of preference. Standard application packs are completed and submitted via the website. The institutions then perform a similar process selecting the candidates they are willing to accept and rank them in order of preference; both ranking orders are blinded to the other party. A central computer is then used to match the prospective applicants with the institutions, based upon their mutual ranking.   Cost of application is tiered depending upon the number of programs you wish to rank, with increasing cost for increasing applications.

Again, the same recommendations for maximising your chances apply regarding visiting institutions and meeting potential future colleagues. Obviously, it takes more effort to visit universities and private practices in America but this shows a high level of commitment and hopefully improves their opinion of your application.

It is important to remember that some programs require the completion of the North American Veterinary Licensing Examination (NAVLE), and it would be advisable to contact the institution/practice in advance of application to ensure you meet the required criteria. There may also be immigration/visa requirements so checking with the US or Canadian Consul/Embassy would be advisable.

Since writing this, David has been successful in his application for a residency, and is due to stay on at the Royal Veterinary College, London, for a further three years to complete his residency training.

VET SCHOOL
5: CLOSING THOUGHTS

Having now written this book in one form or another for several years since graduating myself I have the advantage of having been witness to a number of changes in the profession and have enjoyed discussing these and potential future changes with friends, colleagues and those of you who are looking to tread your own veterinary career path. The veterinary profession is an exciting, rapidly evolving one and we have seen developments across many facets of the sector.

One area of significant change is in the structure of the veterinary industry, with a marked shift from the classic, traditional model of many mixed practices owned and run through partnerships, to the rise of the corporate groups and a shift towards practices being run as companies, owned by directors, not necessarily vets. I personally envisage a future in which larger corporate groups trade, and compete, side by side with fewer but larger, well marketed and managed private veterinary practices. The specialisation that has become commonplace in veterinary, with small, farm and equine clinics instead of mixed practices, will continue, and it may well be that we see further specialisation with even finer fragmentation into specific species-centered services. We already have evidence of this, with clinics that cater solely to cats, for example, or exotics, *or equine* and there is no reason to think that we won't see species specialisation in other areas, such as farm animal work.

The clinical challenges are, some predict, set to increase, with changes in both climate, travel and the relaxation of border controls, such as those seen in the relatively recent pet passport revisions, posed to bring previously "exotic" diseases and parasites to our shores. Knowledge, consideration of and an ability to screen for and manage such conditions will be ever more important parts of our veterinary skill set. Greater acceptance of and willingness to work with other professionals outside of veterinary will become more important as our integration with human health, under the "One Health" banner, becomes more of a priority. The results of this closer working relationship will surely be to the betterment of both human health and our animal charges, and push veterinary knowledge and skills higher up the relative scale of importance.

Veterinary education has, since the opening of the first new vet school in many years at Nottingham, changed, with a general shift away from the rather dry, lecture driven delivery of veterinary education towards a greater emphasis on practical skills and richer, multi-media modes of knowledge transfer and inspiration of undergraduates and postgraduates alike. Who would have envisaged, for example, that we would have at our disposal such valuable tools as virtual cows and e-learning? With another new vet school set to start teaching students very soon and more whispered to be on the cards, the veterinary education sector is,

I believe, set for a period of real change and reformation, with opinions very much divided. Whatever happens, it is imperative that the value of the veterinary degree and that of the qualified veterinary surgeon is fiercely upheld as failing to do so would do a huge disservice to both us as professionals, current students, future vets and those who rely upon our skills and knowledge.

Technology has had a marked impact on many aspects of our profession, from advances in clinical technologies, such as imaging, to marketing and educational tools and platforms. With the ever onward march of technological development the future for how these might translate into practice, and veterinary in general, is one which I particularly enjoy pondering.

If its a life free from stress, challenges and change that you're looking for then a career in veterinary may not be quite right for you. Other far more lucrative sectors, such as banking, law and business, hold the promise of higher pay and the trappings of wealth that you will not readily find as a veterinary graduate but most vets agree that it isn't the material factors that first attracted them to veterinary and continue to motivate them to do a great job.

Veterinary provides its members with a number of things, ranging from a comfortable living, by modern standards, to daily challenges, with a new, unexpected and testing problem just a phone call away, and the ability to diversify and truly vary the course of their careers. There are, of course, drawbacks, as with any career, and the day-to-day life of a traditional vet in practice can, on occasion, be highly stressful, frustrating and lonely, with an unacceptably high suicide and alcoholism rate compared to other professions. Thankfully, the positive aspects of veterinary shine through and it is the immense sense of satisfaction and pride that comes with doing a great job and striving to improve the lives of both animals and owners that drives the profession.

The path to qualification as a vet and beyond is certainly not an easy one and even getting into Vet School is a huge challenge. The amount of hard work, dedication, commitment and determination that go into an application to vet school is colossal and even then, there is no guarantee of a successful outcome. That is why veterinary is not for the faint of heart and you either need your head tested or a medal for choosing to start down the path you have chosen. With more and more options for where to apply, greater competition for work experience placements and a much bigger financial commitment required from you, the need to be certain that you really, truly want to be a vet is as important as it has ever been. The earlier you start your journey the better, and the more prepared and informed you are then the greater are your chances of success. Congratulations on reading this book and using the services of Vet School Success - you've just helped your own cause immensely. Good luck and welcome to one of the most rewarding professions on Planet Earth.

Yours in nerdiness and vettiness

Christopher Shivelton Queen BSc BVSc MRCVS

VET SCHOOL

APPENDIX I

Veterinary Schools

Rather than give you a pointless list of addresses and contact numbers, all of which can be easily found on the vet schools' websites, I have provided a quick reference for the universities' websites:

Royal Veterinary College (RVC), London	www.rvc.ac.uk
Cambridge Veterinary School	www.vet.cam.ac.uk
Faculty of Veterinary Science, Liverpool	www.liv.ac.uk/vets
Nottingham School of Veterinary Medicine & Science	www.nottingham.ac.uk/vets
The Royal (Dick) School of Veterinary Studies, Edinburgh	www.vet.ed.ac.uk
University of Glasgow Veterinary School	www.gla.ac.uk/vet

Bristol School of Veterinary Science	www.vetschool.ac.uk
University of Surrey, Guildford	www.surrey.ac.uk
Faculty of Veterinary Medicine, University College, Dublin	www.ucd.ie/vetmed
St George's School of Veterinary Medicine, Granada, West Indies	www.sgu.edu/school-of-veterinary-medicine

Useful Websites

1. Royal College of Veterinary Surgeons (www.rcvs.org.uk)

The RCVS also have a careers page, which offers advice and useful links to other helpful and interesting websites (www.rcvs.org.uk/careers)

2. DEFRA (www.defra.gov.uk)

3. UCAS (www.ucas.ac.uk)

4. BMAT (www.bmat.org.uk)

VET SCHOOL

APPENDIX 2

UK Vet School Admissions 2011/2012

UK Vet School Students		Veterinary students taking an intercalated science course in 2011/2012			Numbers of intercalated degree holders (2)			Numbers of students obtaining a veterinary degree in 2011			Total numbers attending the veterinary course(1)		
		M	F	Total	M	F	Total	M	F	Total	M	F	Total
Bristol	UK	2	13	15	8	36	44	19	84	105	119	403	552
	EU	0	0		0	0		0	1		5	13	
	Overseas	0	0		0	0		0	1		1	11	
Cambridge	UK	0	0	0	0	0	0	14	44	60	94	289	400
	EU	0	0		0	0		0	1		1	6	
	Overseas	0	0		0	0		0	1		0	10	
Edinburgh	UK	2	2	5	0	0	0	16	63	126	95	340	754
	EU	1	0		0	0		1	5		6	28	
	Overseas	0	0		0	0		6	35		51	234	
Glasgow	UK	0	2	2	0	6	6	24	42	104	118	247	596
	EU	0	0		0	0		1	0		1	4	
	Overseas	0	0		0	0		7	30		53	173	
	UK	1	10		1	5		20	99		125	468	